EYEWITNESS VISUAL DICTIONARIES

THE VISUAL DICTIONARY *of the* HUMAN BODY

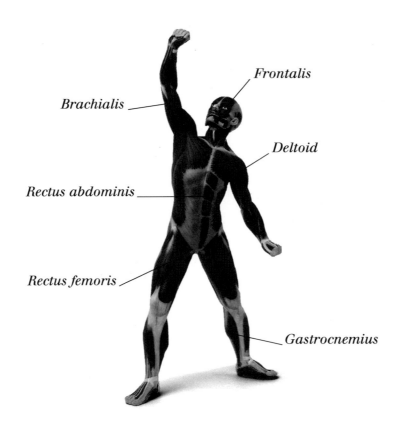

Brachialis

Frontalis

Deltoid

Rectus abdominis

Rectus femoris

Gastrocnemius

SUPERFICIAL SKELETAL MUSCLES

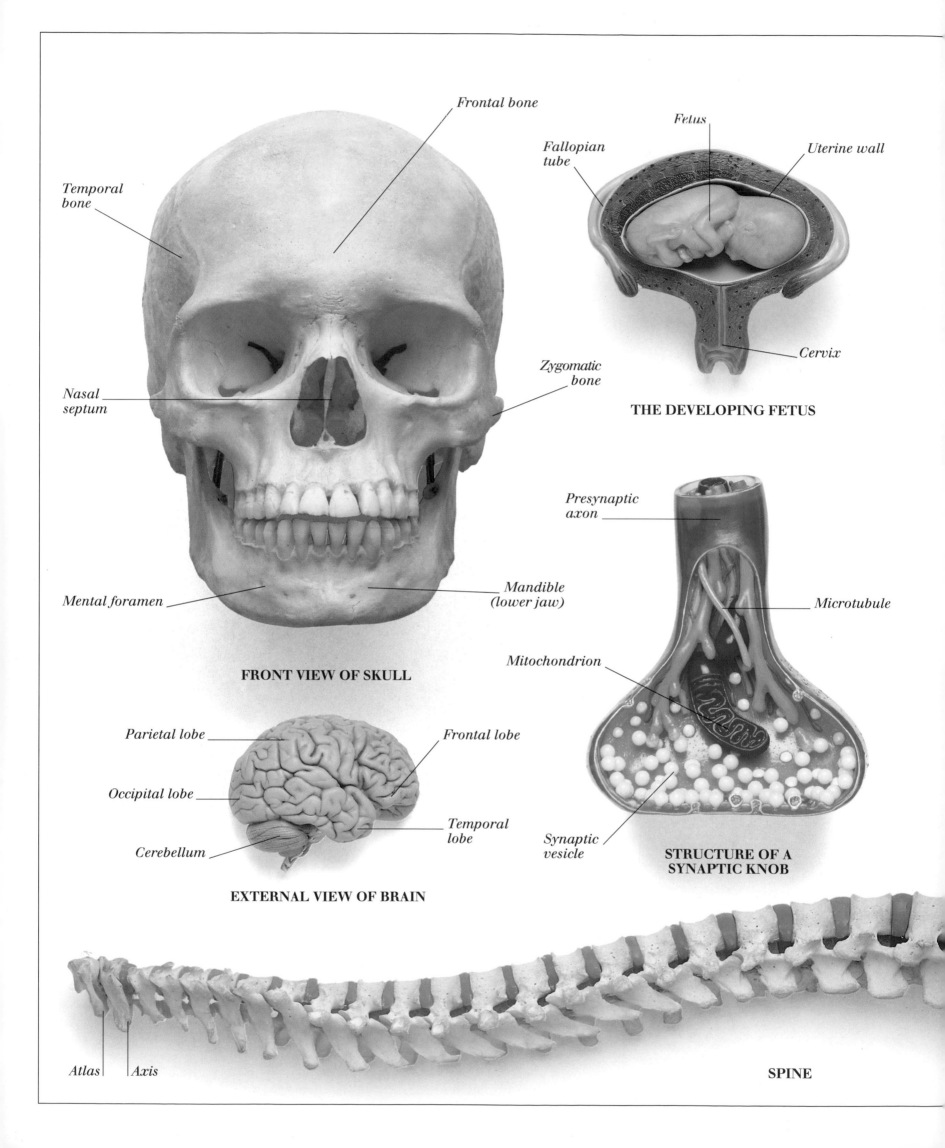

Frontal bone

Temporal bone

Nasal septum

Mental foramen

Zygomatic bone

Mandible (lower jaw)

FRONT VIEW OF SKULL

Fetus

Fallopian tube

Uterine wall

Cervix

THE DEVELOPING FETUS

Presynaptic axon

Microtubule

Mitochondrion

Synaptic vesicle

STRUCTURE OF A SYNAPTIC KNOB

Parietal lobe

Frontal lobe

Occipital lobe

Temporal lobe

Cerebellum

EXTERNAL VIEW OF BRAIN

Atlas

Axis

SPINE

THE VISUAL
DICTIONARY *of the*
HUMAN
BODY

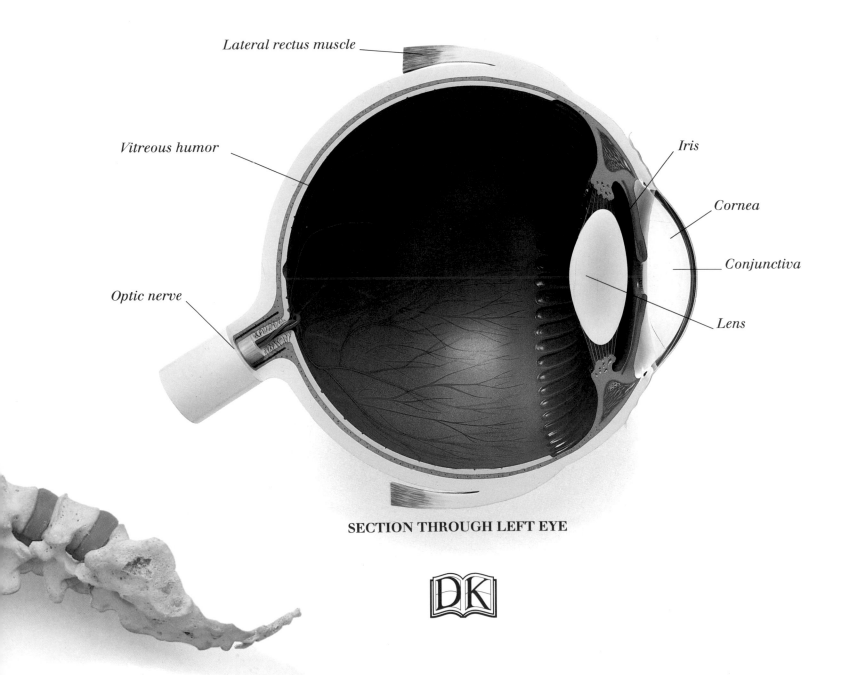

Lateral rectus muscle

Vitreous humor

Iris

Cornea

Conjunctiva

Lens

Optic nerve

SECTION THROUGH LEFT EYE

DK

PROJECT ART EDITOR BRYN WALLS
DESIGNERS DUNCAN BROWN, SIMONE END, NICKI LIDDIARD

PROJECT EDITOR MARY LINDSAY
CONSULTANT EDITORS RICHARD CUMMINS, FRCS, DR FIONA PAYNE, DR FRANCES WILLIAMS

SERIES ART EDITOR PAUL WILKINSON
ART DIRECTOR CHEZ PICTHALL
MANAGING EDITOR RUTH MIDGLEY

PHOTOGRAPHY PETER CHADWICK, GEOFF DANN, DAVE KING

PRODUCTION HILARY STEPHENS

SPECIAL THANKS TO THAD YABLONSKY

ANATOMICAL MODELS SUPPLIED BY SOMSO MODELLE, COBURG, GERMANY

Superior vena cava — — Aorta

Right ventricle — — Left ventricle

CIRCULATORY SYSTEM OF HEART AND LUNGS

FIRST AMERICAN EDITION, 1991

030-AI601-Nov/02
20 19

PUBLISHED IN THE UNITED STATES BY
DORLING KINDERSLEY, INC., 345 HUDSON ST.
NEW YORK, NEW YORK 10014

ISBN: 978-1-8794-3118-8

LIBRARY OF CONGRESS CARD CATALOG NUMBER: 91-060899

REPRODUCTION BY COLOURSCAN, SINGAPORE
Printed and bound in China by Leo Paper Products Ltd

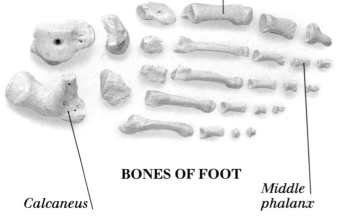

Metatarsal

Calcaneus

Middle phalanx

BONES OF FOOT

Contents

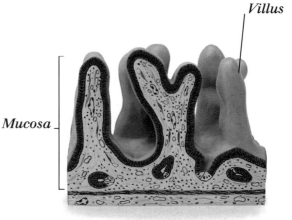

Villus

Mucosa

INTERNAL SURFACE OF JEJUNUM

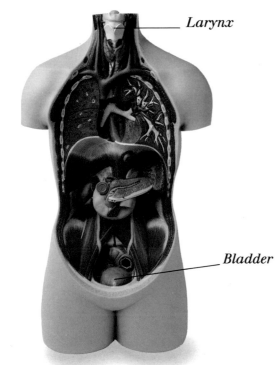

Larynx

Bladder

**CHEST AND ABDOMINAL CAVITIES
WITH SOME ORGANS REMOVED**

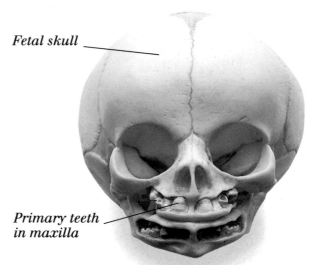

Fetal skull

Primary teeth in maxilla

**DEVELOPMENT OF
TEETH IN A FETUS**

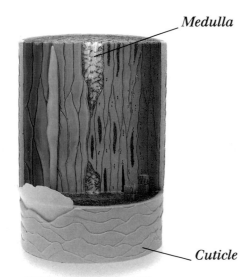

Medulla

Cuticle

SECTION OF HAIR

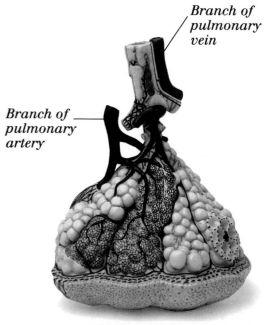

Branch of pulmonary vein

Branch of pulmonary artery

BRONCHIOLE WITH LOBULE

The human body

ALTHOUGH THERE IS enormous
variation between the external
appearances of humans, all bodies
contain the same basic features.
The outward form of the
human body depends on the
size of the skeleton, the shape
of the muscles, the thickness
of the fat layer beneath
the skin, the elasticity or
sagginess of the skin, and
the person's age and
gender. Males tend to be taller
than females, with broader
shoulders, more body hair,
and a different pattern of fat
deposits under the skin; the
female body tends to be
less muscular and has
a shallower and wider
pelvis to allow
for childbirth.

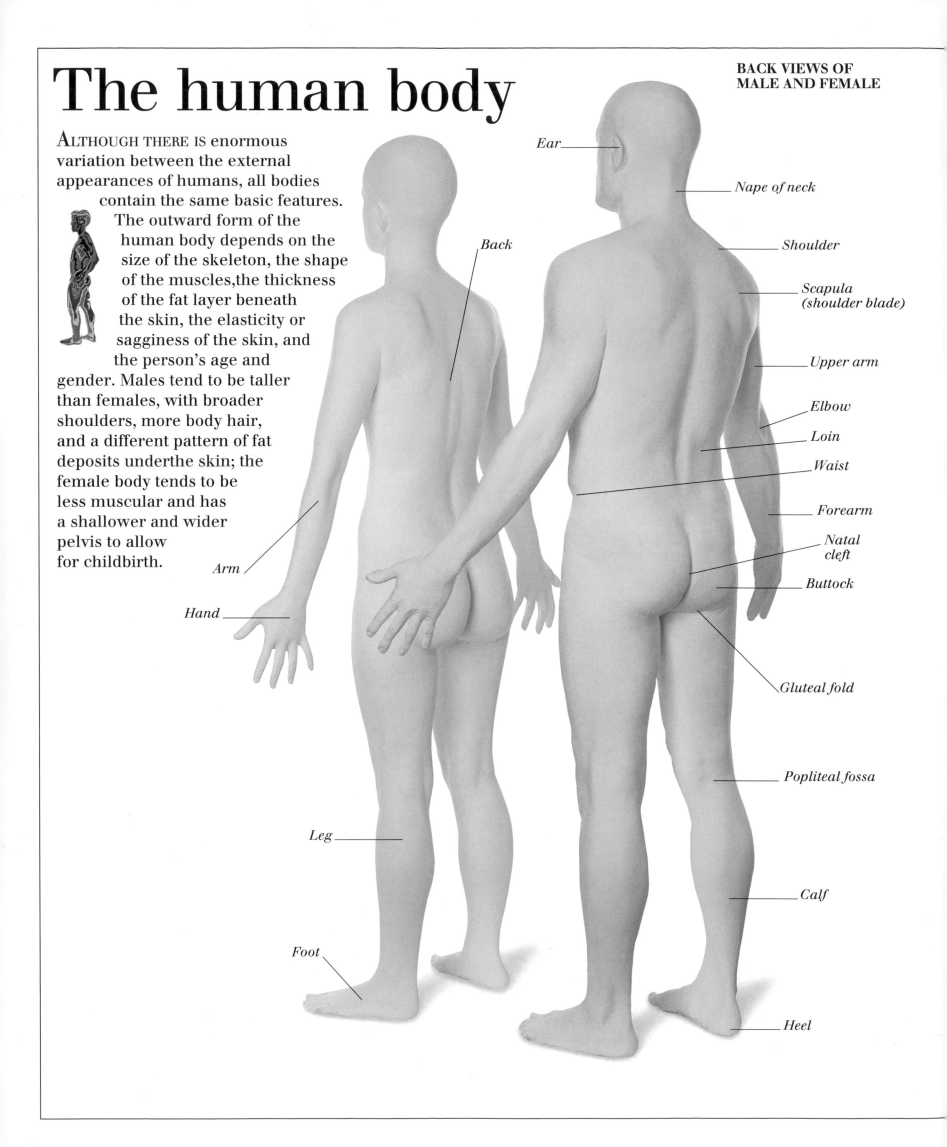

Ear

Nape of neck

Shoulder

*Scapula
(shoulder blade)*

Upper arm

Elbow

Loin

Waist

Forearm

*Natal
cleft*

Buttock

Gluteal fold

Popliteal fossa

Calf

Heel

Back

Arm

Hand

Leg

Foot

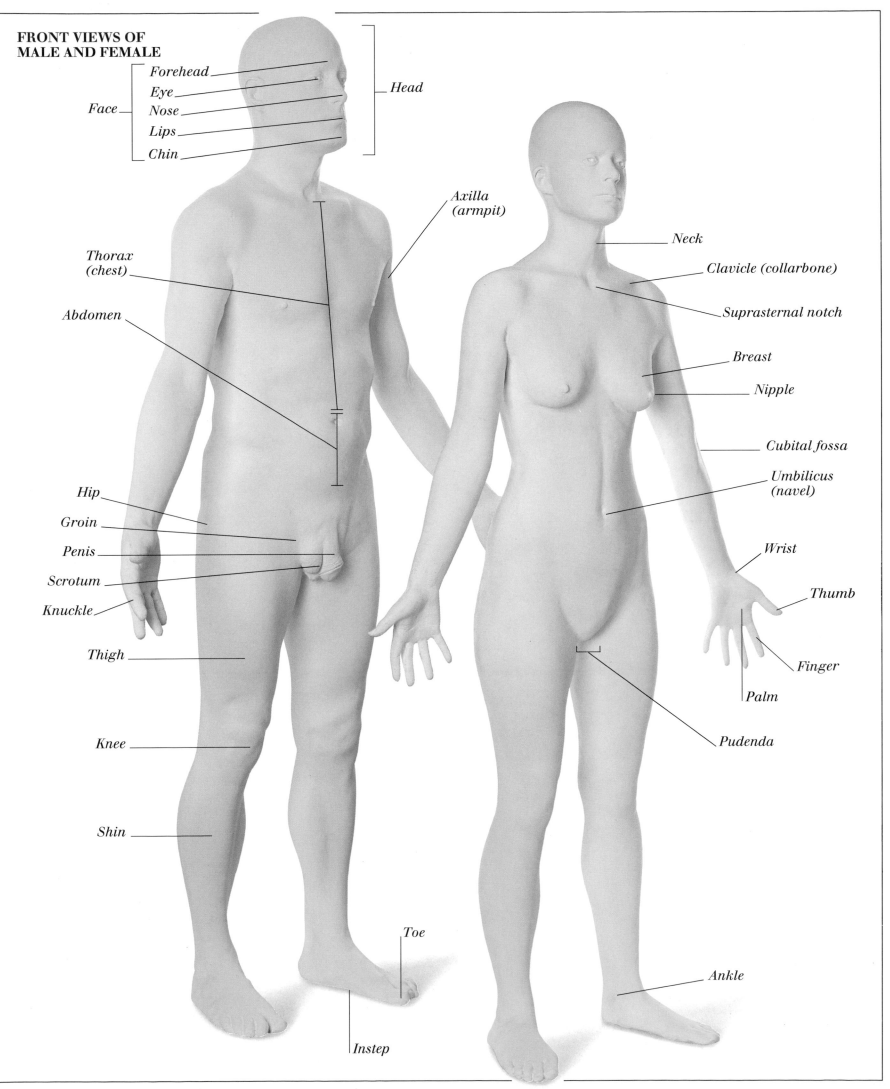

FRONT VIEWS OF MALE AND FEMALE

Forehead

Eye

Face

Nose

Lips

Chin

Head

Axilla (armpit)

Thorax (chest)

Abdomen

Neck

Clavicle (collarbone)

Suprasternal notch

Breast

Nipple

Cubital fossa

Umbilicus (navel)

Hip

Groin

Penis

Scrotum

Knuckle

Wrist

Thumb

Thigh

Finger

Palm

Knee

Pudenda

Shin

Toe

Ankle

Instep

Head

IN A NEWBORN BABY, the head accounts for one-quarter of the total body length; by adulthood, the proportion has reduced to one-eighth. Contained in the head are the body's main sense organs: eyes, ears, olfactory nerves that detect smells, and the taste buds of the tongue. Signals from these organs pass to the body's great coordination center: the brain, housed in the protective, bony dome of the skull. Hair on the head insulates against heat loss, and adult males also grow thick facial hair. The face has three important openings: two nostrils through which air passes, and the mouth, which takes in nourishment and helps form speech. Although all heads are basically similar, differences in the size, shape, and color of features produce an infinite variety of appearances.

SIDE VIEW OF EXTERNAL FEATURES OF HEAD

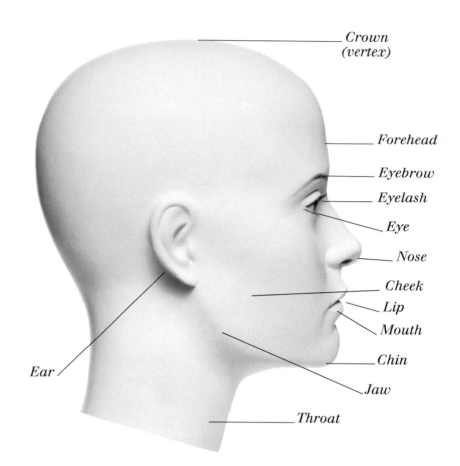

Crown (vertex)
Forehead
Eyebrow
Eyelash
Eye
Nose
Cheek
Lip
Mouth
Chin
Jaw
Ear
Throat

SECTION THROUGH HEAD

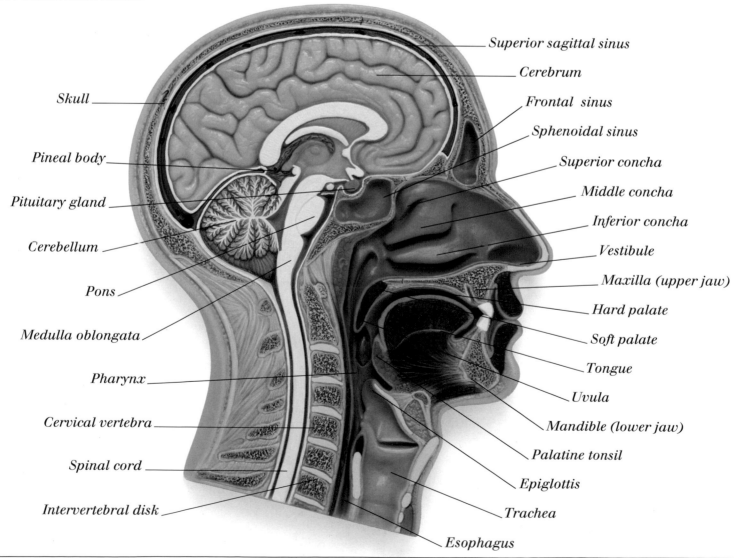

Skull
Pineal body
Pituitary gland
Cerebellum
Pons
Medulla oblongata
Pharynx
Cervical vertebra
Spinal cord
Intervertebral disk

Superior sagittal sinus
Cerebrum
Frontal sinus
Sphenoidal sinus
Superior concha
Middle concha
Inferior concha
Vestibule
Maxilla (upper jaw)
Hard palate
Soft palate
Tongue
Uvula
Mandible (lower jaw)
Palatine tonsil
Epiglottis
Trachea
Esophagus

**FRONT VIEW OF EXTERNAL
FEATURES OF HEAD**

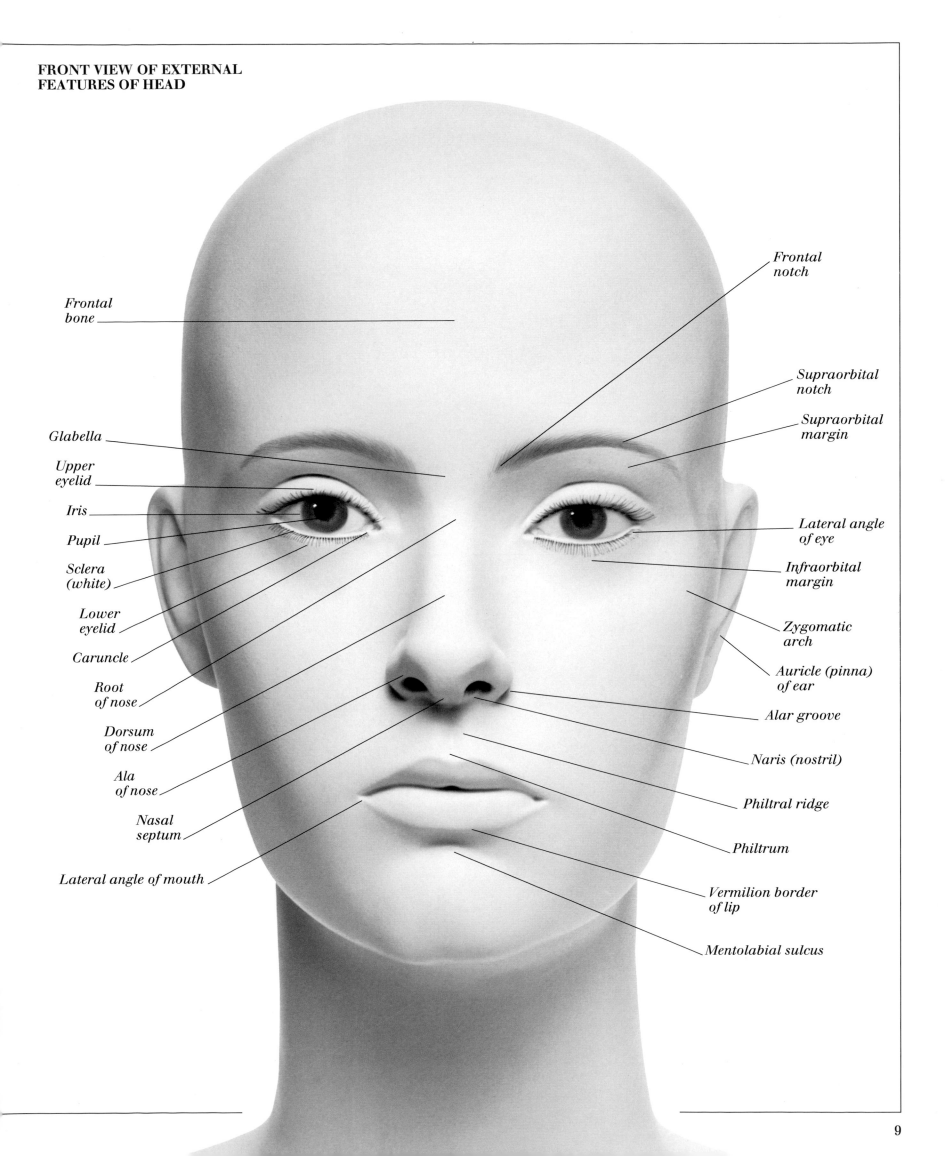

Frontal
notch

Supraorbital
notch

Supraorbital
margin

Frontal
bone

Lateral angle
of eye

Infraorbital
margin

Zygomatic
arch

Auricle (pinna)
of ear

Alar groove

Naris (nostril)

Philtral ridge

Philtrum

Vermilion border
of lip

Mentolabial sulcus

Glabella

Upper
eyelid

Iris

Pupil

Sclera
(white)

Lower
eyelid

Caruncle

Root
of nose

Dorsum
of nose

Ala
of nose

Nasal
septum

Lateral angle of mouth

Body organs

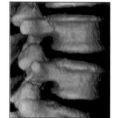

ALL THE VITAL BODY ORGANS except for the brain are enclosed within the trunk or torso (the body apart from the head and limbs). The trunk contains two large cavities separated by a muscular sheet called the diaphragm. The upper cavity, known as the thorax or chest cavity, contains the heart and lungs. The lower cavity, called the abdominal cavity, contains the stomach, intestines, liver, and pancreas, which all play a role in digesting food. Also within the trunk are the kidneys and bladder, which are part of the urinary system, and the reproductive organs, which hold the seeds of new human life. Modern imaging techniques, such as contrast X-rays and different types of scans, make it possible to see and study body organs without the need to cut through their protective coverings of skin, fat, muscle, and bone.

MAJOR INTERNAL STRUCTURES

Thyroid gland

Larynx

Heart

Right lung

Left lung

Diaphragm

Liver

Stomach

Large intestine

Small intestine

Greater omentum

IMAGING THE BODY

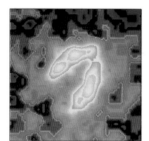

SCINTIGRAM OF HEART CHAMBERS

ANGIOGRAM OF RIGHT LUNG

CONTRAST X-RAY OF GALLBLADDER

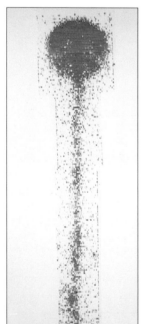

SCINTIGRAM OF NERVOUS SYSTEM

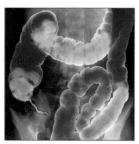

DOUBLE CONTRAST X-RAY OF COLON

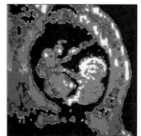

ULTRASOUND SCAN OF TWINS IN UTERUS

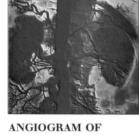

ANGIOGRAM OF KIDNEYS

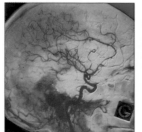

ANGIOGRAM OF ARTERIES OF HEAD

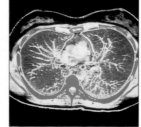

CT SCAN THROUGH FEMALE CHEST

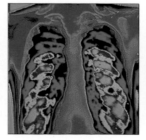

THERMOGRAM OF CHEST REGION

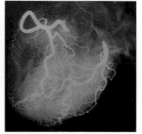

ANGIOGRAM OF ARTERIES OF HEART

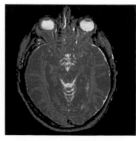

MRI SCAN THROUGH HEAD AT EYE LEVEL

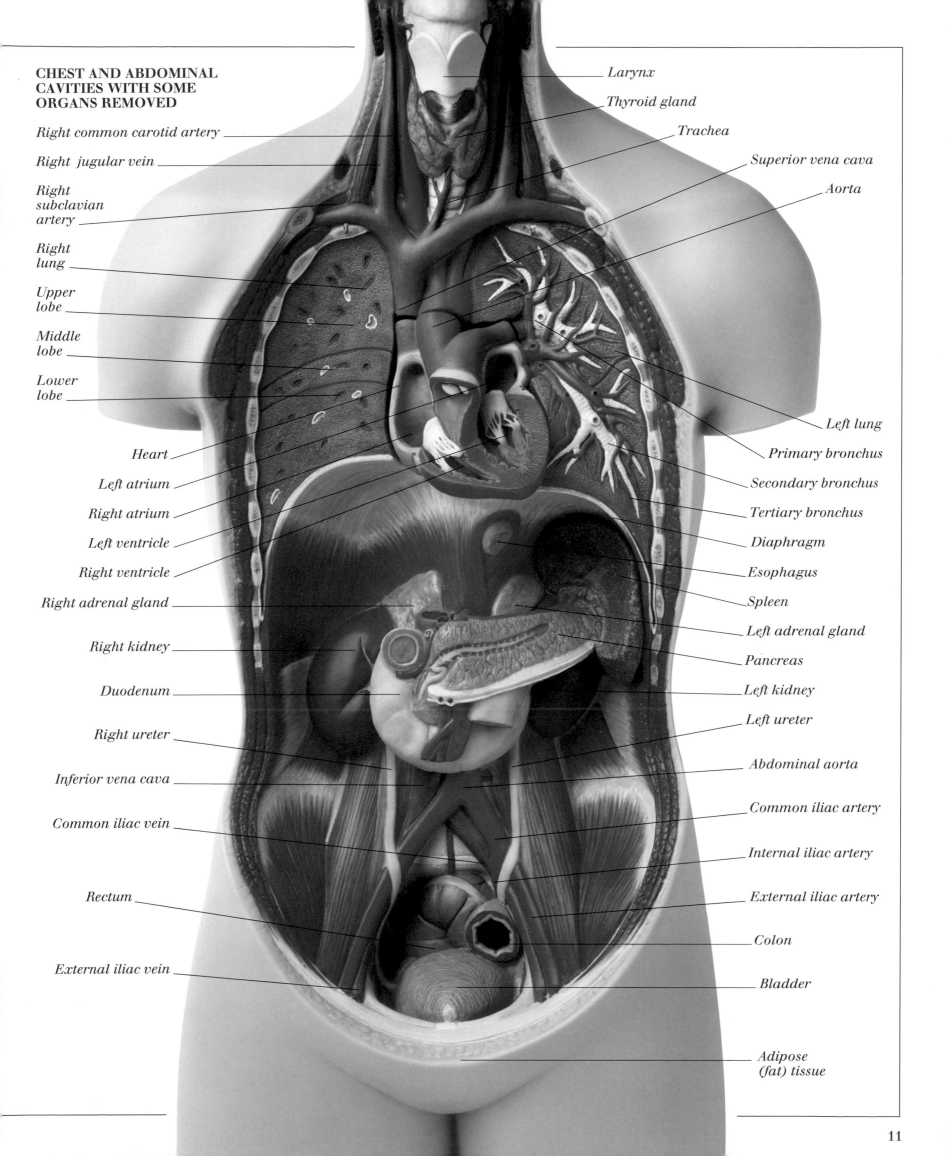

CHEST AND ABDOMINAL CAVITIES WITH SOME ORGANS REMOVED

Larynx

Thyroid gland

Trachea

Superior vena cava

Aorta

Right common carotid artery

Right jugular vein

Right subclavian artery

Right lung

Upper lobe

Middle lobe

Lower lobe

Left lung

Primary bronchus

Secondary bronchus

Tertiary bronchus

Heart

Left atrium

Right atrium

Left ventricle

Right ventricle

Diaphragm

Esophagus

Spleen

Right adrenal gland

Left adrenal gland

Pancreas

Right kidney

Duodenum

Left kidney

Right ureter

Left ureter

Inferior vena cava

Abdominal aorta

Common iliac vein

Common iliac artery

Internal iliac artery

Rectum

External iliac artery

Colon

External iliac vein

Bladder

Adipose (fat) tissue

Body cells

EVERYONE IS MADE UP OF BILLIONS OF CELLS, which are the basic structural units of the body. Bones, muscles, nerves, skin, blood, and all other body tissues are formed from different types of cells. Each cell has a specific function but works with other types of cells to perform the enormous number of tasks needed to sustain life. Most body cells have a similar basic structure. Each cell has an outer layer (called the cell membrane) and contains a fluid material (cytoplasm). Within the cytoplasm are many specialized structures (organelles). The most important organelle is the nucleus, which contains vital genetic material and acts as the cell's control center.

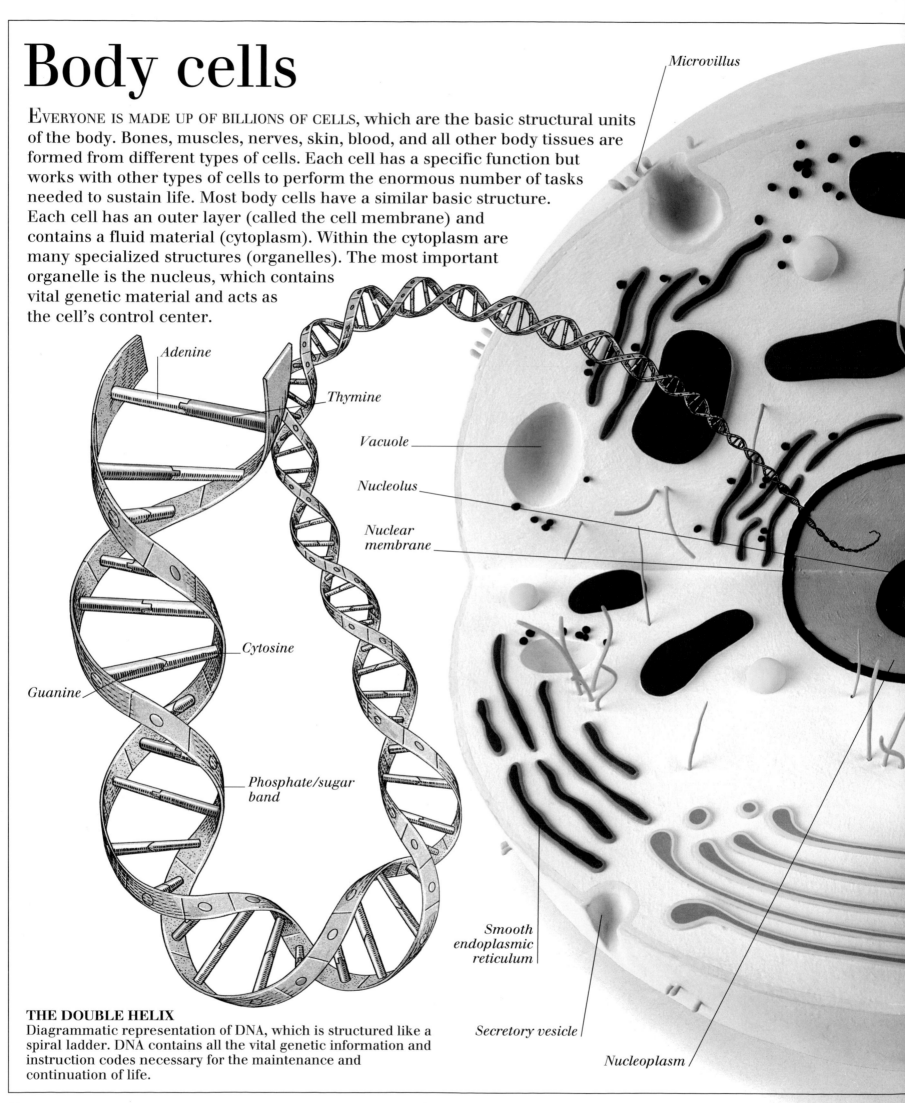

Microvillus

Adenine

Thymine

Vacuole

Nucleolus

Nuclear membrane

Cytosine

Guanine

Phosphate/sugar band

Smooth endoplasmic reticulum

Secretory vesicle

Nucleoplasm

THE DOUBLE HELIX
Diagrammatic representation of DNA, which is structured like a spiral ladder. DNA contains all the vital genetic information and instruction codes necessary for the maintenance and continuation of life.

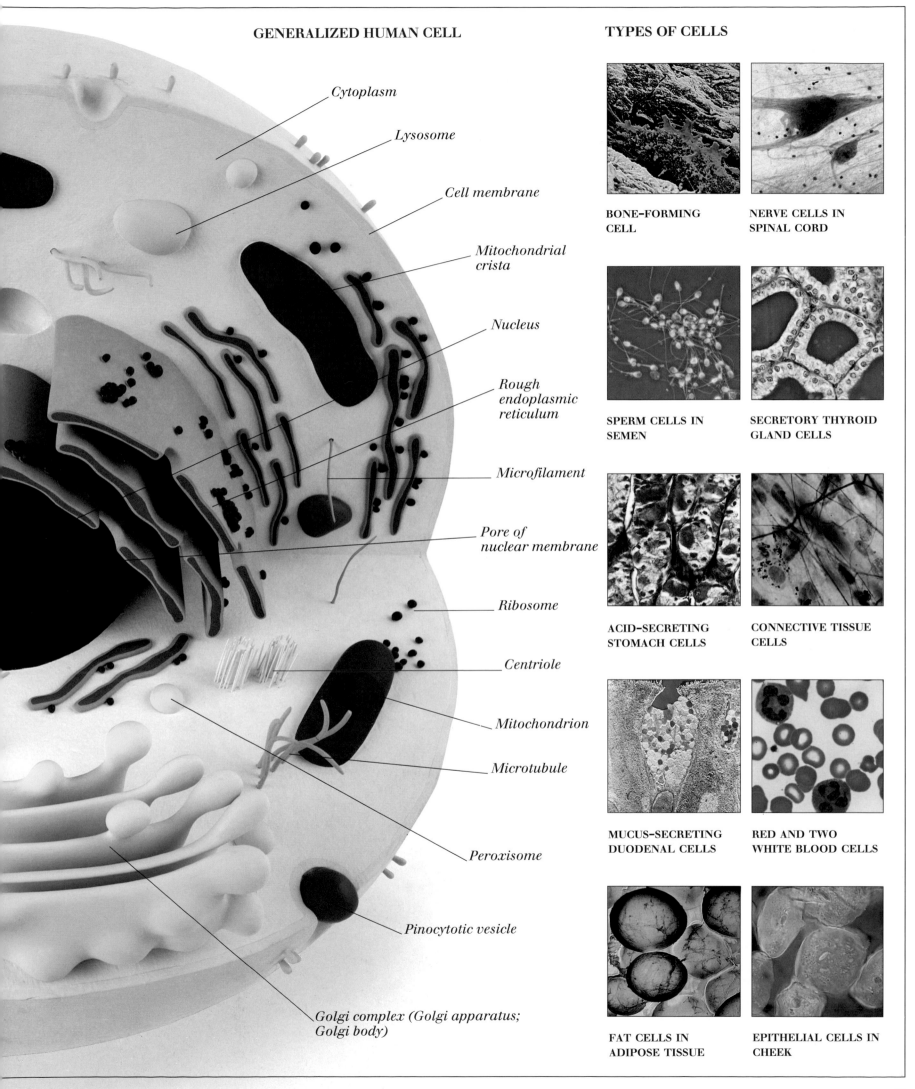

GENERALIZED HUMAN CELL

Cytoplasm

Lysosome

Cell membrane

Mitochondrial crista

Nucleus

Rough endoplasmic reticulum

Microfilament

Pore of nuclear membrane

Ribosome

Centriole

Mitochondrion

Microtubule

Peroxisome

Pinocytotic vesicle

Golgi complex (Golgi apparatus; Golgi body)

TYPES OF CELLS

BONE-FORMING CELL

NERVE CELLS IN SPINAL CORD

SPERM CELLS IN SEMEN

SECRETORY THYROID GLAND CELLS

ACID-SECRETING STOMACH CELLS

CONNECTIVE TISSUE CELLS

MUCUS-SECRETING DUODENAL CELLS

RED AND TWO WHITE BLOOD CELLS

FAT CELLS IN ADIPOSE TISSUE

EPITHELIAL CELLS IN CHEEK

Skeleton

THE SKELETON IS A MOBILE FRAMEWORK made up of 206 bones, approximately half of which are in the hands and feet. Although individual bones are rigid, the skeleton as a whole is remarkably flexible and allows the human body a huge range of movement. The skeleton serves as an anchorage for the skeletal muscles, and as a protective cage for the body's internal organs. Female bones are usually smaller and lighter than male bones, and the female pelvis is shallower and has a wider cavity.

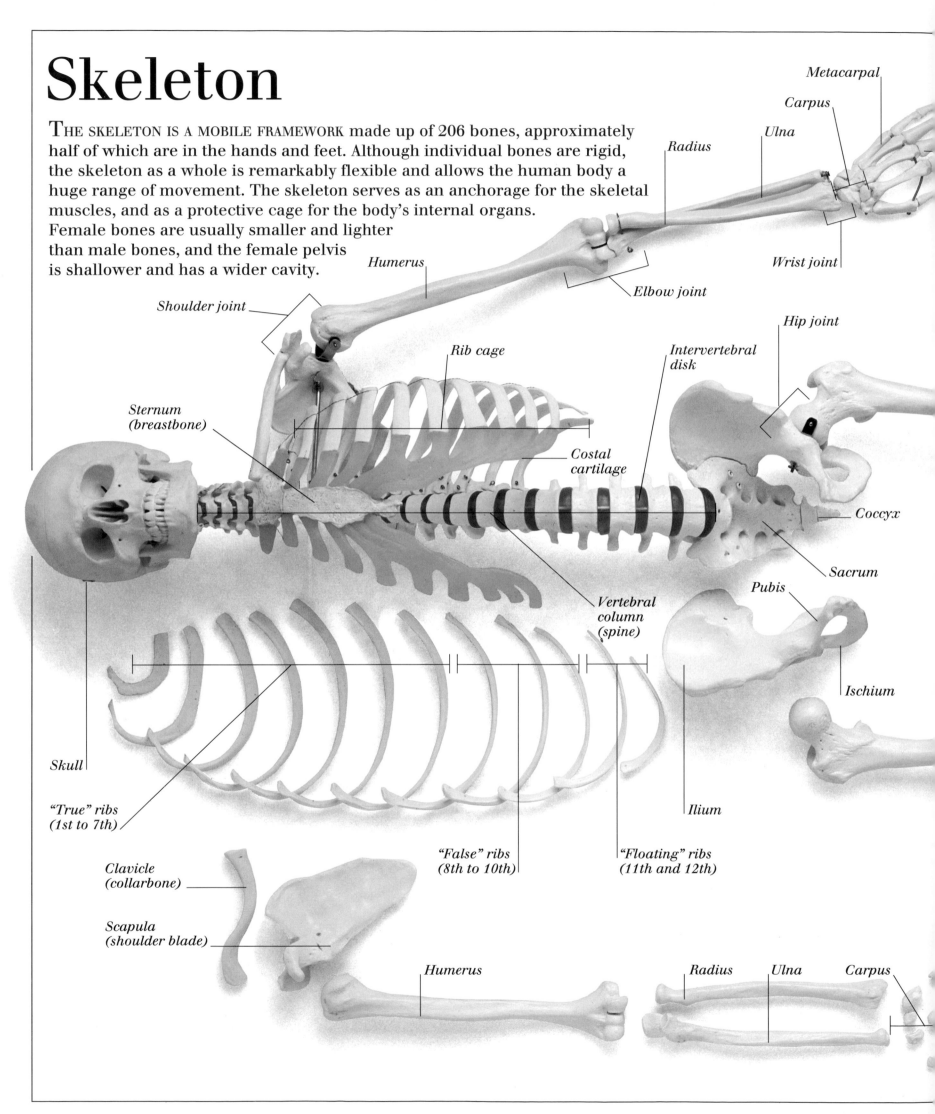

Metacarpal

Carpus

Ulna

Radius

Humerus

Shoulder joint

Wrist joint

Elbow joint

Hip joint

Rib cage

Intervertebral disk

Sternum (breastbone)

Costal cartilage

Coccyx

Sacrum

Pubis

Vertebral column (spine)

Ischium

Skull

Ilium

"True" ribs (1st to 7th)

"False" ribs (8th to 10th)

"Floating" ribs (11th and 12th)

Clavicle (collarbone)

Scapula (shoulder blade)

Humerus

Radius

Ulna

Carpus

Distal phalanx

Middle phalanx

Proximal phalanx

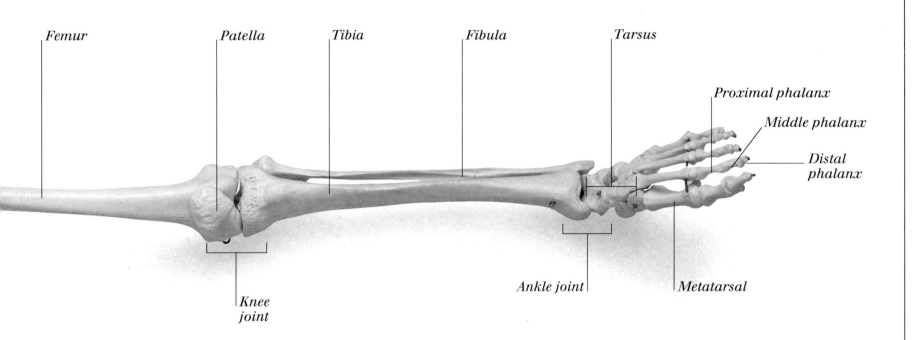

Femur   Patella   Tibia   Fibula   Tarsus

Proximal phalanx

Middle phalanx

Distal phalanx

Ankle joint   Metatarsal

Knee joint

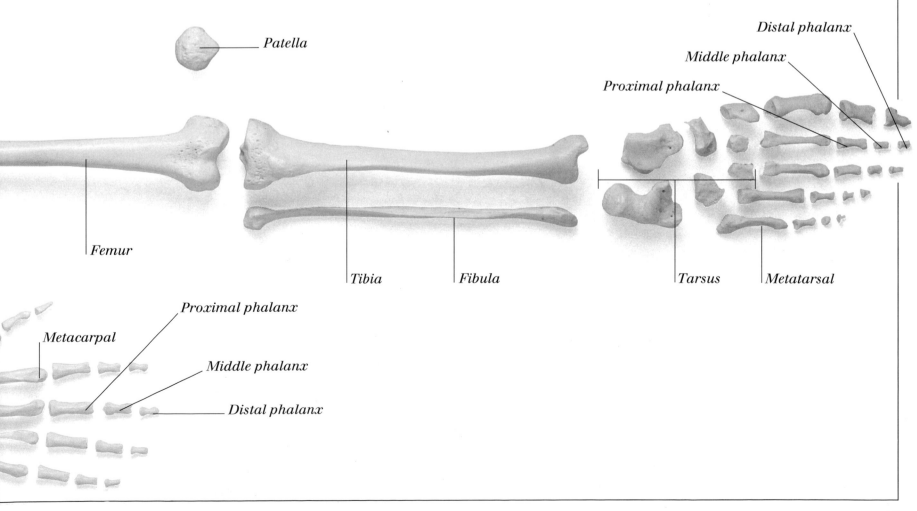

Patella

Distal phalanx

Middle phalanx

Proximal phalanx

Femur

Tibia   Fibula

Tarsus   Metatarsal

Proximal phalanx

Metacarpal

Middle phalanx

Distal phalanx

Skull

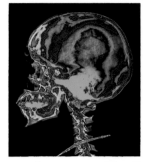

THE SKULL is the most complicated bony structure of the body—but every feature serves a purpose. Internally, the main hollow chamber of the skull has three levels that support the brain, with every bump and hollow corresponding to the shape of the brain. Underneath and toward the back of the skull is a large round hole, called the foramen magnum, through which the spinal cord passes. To the front of this are many smaller openings through which nerves, arteries, and veins pass to and from the brain. The roof of the skull is formed from four thin, curved bones that are firmly fixed together from the age of about two years. At the front of the skull are two orbits, which contain the eyeballs, and a central hole for the airway of the nose. The jawbone hinges on either side of the skull at ear level.

RIGHT SIDE VIEW OF A FETAL SKULL

Anterior fontanelle

Parietal bone

Coronal suture

Frontal bone

Nasal bone

Mental symphysis

Lambdoid suture

Occipital bone

Mastoid fontanelle

External auditory meatus

Sphenoidal fontanelle

RIGHT SIDE VIEW OF SKULL

Greater wing of sphenoid bone

Coronal suture

Frontal bone

Frontozygomatic suture

Parietal bone

Supraorbital margin

Squamous suture

Orbital cavity

Nasal bone

Anterior nasal spine

Maxilla (upper jaw)

Lambdoid suture

Occipital bone

Mandible (lower jaw)

Temporal bone

External auditory meatus

Condyle

Coronoid process

Zygomatic bone

Mastoid process

Mental foramen

VIEW OF SKULL FROM BELOW

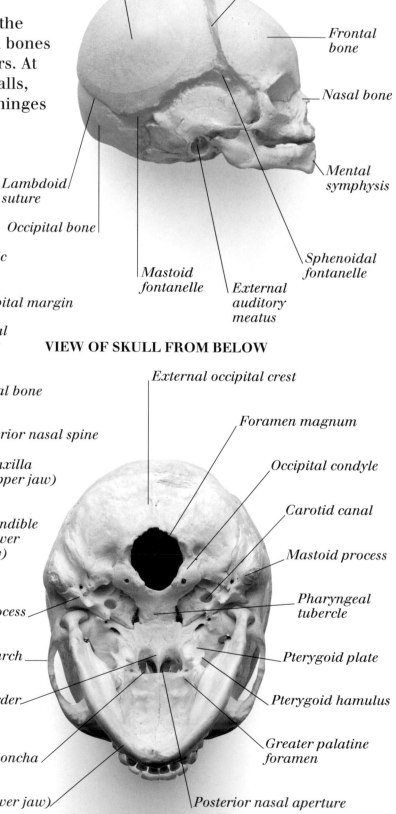

External occipital crest

Foramen magnum

Occipital condyle

Carotid canal

Mastoid process

Pharyngeal tubercle

Pterygoid plate

Styloid process

Zygomatic arch

Pterygoid hamulus

Posterior border of vomer

Greater palatine foramen

Concha

Posterior nasal aperture

Mandible (lower jaw)

FRONT VIEW OF SKULL

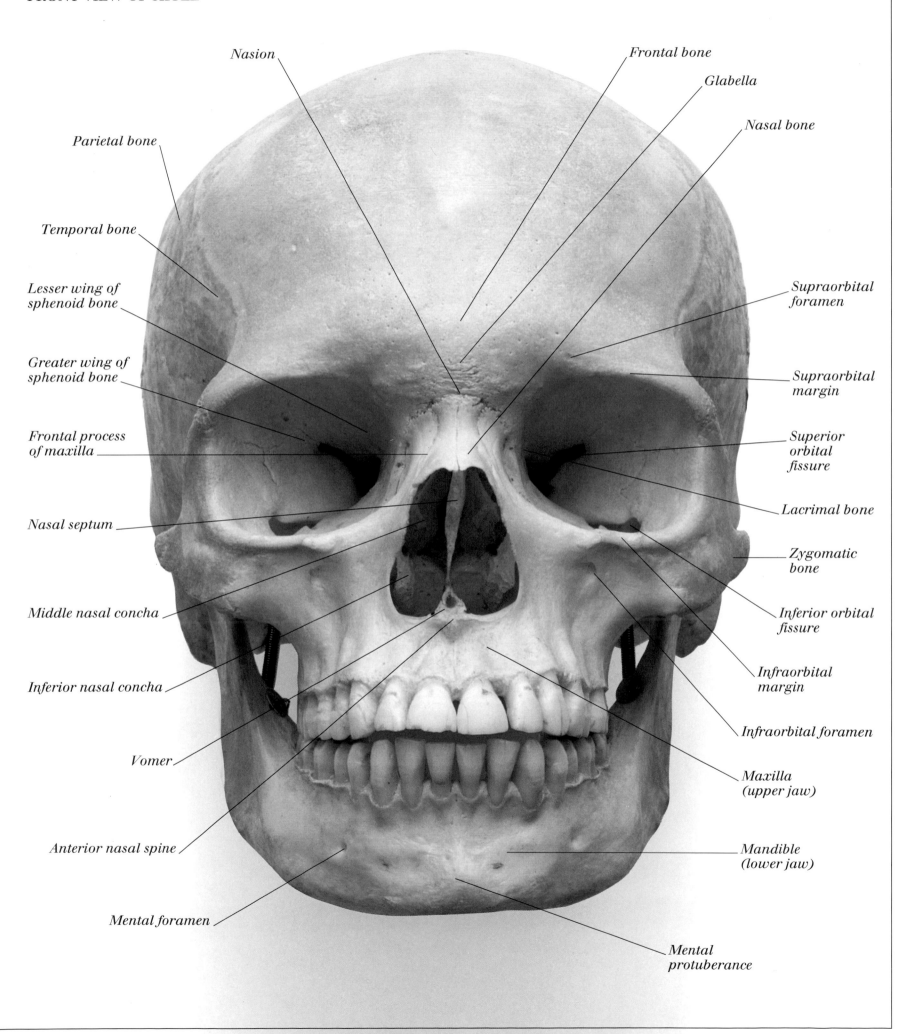

Nasion

Frontal bone

Glabella

Nasal bone

Parietal bone

Temporal bone

Lesser wing of
sphenoid bone

Greater wing of
sphenoid bone

Frontal process
of maxilla

Nasal septum

Middle nasal concha

Inferior nasal concha

Vomer

Anterior nasal spine

Mental foramen

Supraorbital
foramen

Supraorbital
margin

Superior
orbital
fissure

Lacrimal bone

Zygomatic
bone

Inferior orbital
fissure

Infraorbital
margin

Infraorbital foramen

Maxilla
(upper jaw)

Mandible
(lower jaw)

Mental
protuberance

Spine

THE SPINE (OR SPINAL COLUMN) has two main functions: it serves as a protective surrounding for the delicate spinal cord and forms the supporting backbone of the skeleton. The spine consists of 24 separate, differently shaped bones (vertebrae) with a curved, triangular bone (the sacrum) at the bottom. The sacrum is made up of fused vertebrae; at its lower end is a small tail-like structure made up of tiny bones collectively called the coccyx. Between each pair of vertebrae is a disk of cartilage that cushions the bones during movement. The top two vertebrae differ in appearance from the others and work as a pair: the first, called the atlas, rotates around a stout vertical peg on the second, called the axis. This arrangement allows the skull to move freely up and down, and from side to side.

SPINE DIVIDED INTO VERTEBRAL SECTIONS

FRONTAL VIEW

Cervical vertebrae

Thoracic vertebrae

Lumbar vertebrae

Sacral vertebrae

Coccygeal vertebrae

TYPES OF VERTEBRAE

ATLAS

Anterior arch

Anterior tubercle

Vertebral foramen

Transverse process

Lateral mass with superior articular facet

Posterior arch

Posterior tubercle

Transverse foramen

AXIS

Facet

Dens

Vertebral foramen

Spinous process

Lamina

Transverse process and foramen

CERVICAL VERTEBRA

Body

Anterior tubercle

Posterior tubercle

Superior articular process

Spinous process

Vertebral foramen

Transverse foramen

SKULL AND SPINE

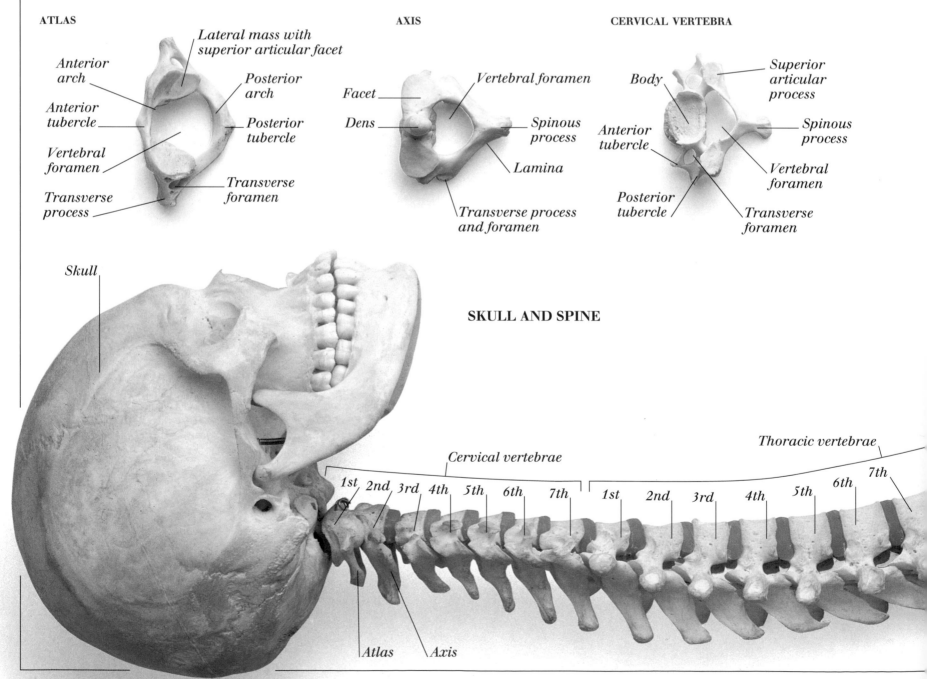

Skull

Cervical vertebrae

1st 2nd 3rd 4th 5th 6th 7th

Atlas Axis

Thoracic vertebrae

1st 2nd 3rd 4th 5th 6th 7th

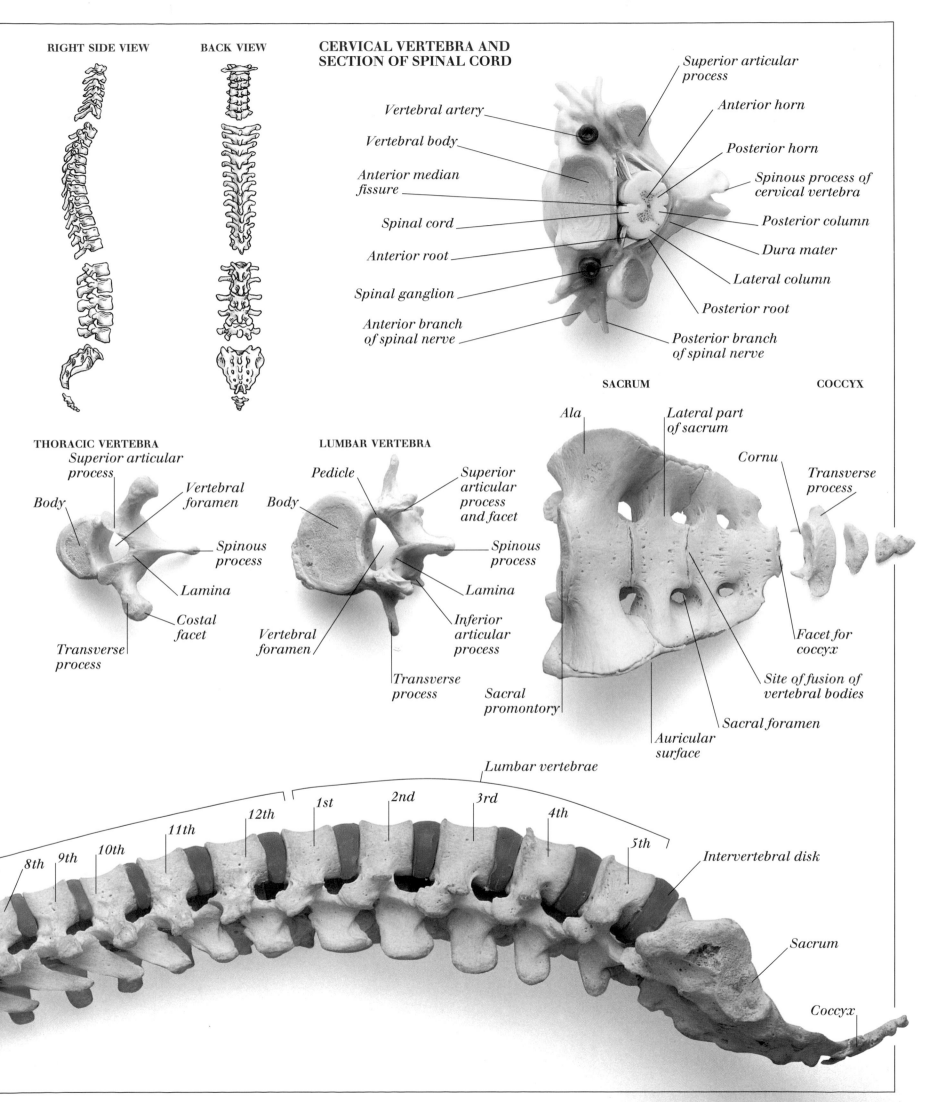

RIGHT SIDE VIEW

BACK VIEW

**CERVICAL VERTEBRA AND
SECTION OF SPINAL CORD**

Vertebral artery

Vertebral body

Anterior median
fissure

Spinal cord

Anterior root

Spinal ganglion

Anterior branch
of spinal nerve

Superior articular
process

Anterior horn

Posterior horn

Spinous process of
cervical vertebra

Posterior column

Dura mater

Lateral column

Posterior root

Posterior branch
of spinal nerve

THORACIC VERTEBRA

Superior articular
process

Body

Vertebral
foramen

Spinous
process

Lamina

Costal
facet

Transverse
process

LUMBAR VERTEBRA

Pedicle

Body

Superior
articular
process
and facet

Spinous
process

Lamina

Inferior
articular
process

Transverse
process

Vertebral
foramen

Sacral
promontory

SACRUM

Ala

Lateral part
of sacrum

Auricular
surface

Sacral foramen

Site of fusion of
vertebral bodies

COCCYX

Cornu

Transverse
process

Facet for
coccyx

Lumbar vertebrae

1st   2nd   3rd   4th

12th   5th

11th

10th

9th

8th

Intervertebral disk

Sacrum

Coccyx

Bones and joints

BONES FORM the body's hard, strong skeletal framework. Each bone has a hard, compact exterior surrounding a spongy, lighter interior. The long bones of the arms and legs, such as the femur (thigh bone), have a central cavity containing bone marrow. Bones are composed chiefly of calcium, phosphorus, and a fibrous substance known as collagen. Bones meet at joints, which are of several different types. For example, the hip is a ball-and-socket joint that allows the femur a wide range of movement, whereas finger joints are simple hinge joints that allow only bending and straightening. Joints are held in place by bands of tissue called ligaments. Movement of joints is facilitated by the smooth hyaline cartilage that covers the bone ends and by the synovial membrane that lines and lubricates the joint.

LIGAMENTS SURROUNDING HIP JOINT

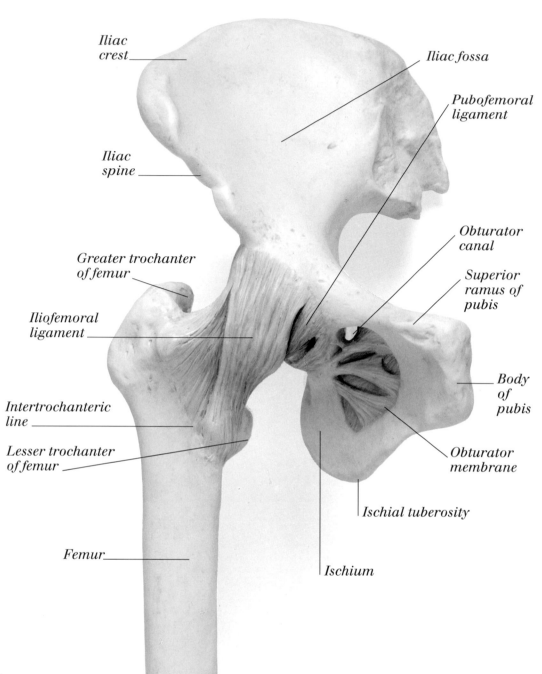

Iliac crest

Iliac fossa

Pubofemoral ligament

Iliac spine

Greater trochanter of femur

Iliofemoral ligament

Obturator canal

Superior ramus of pubis

Body of pubis

Intertrochanteric line

Lesser trochanter of femur

Obturator membrane

Ischial tuberosity

Femur

Ischium

SECTION THROUGH LEFT FEMUR

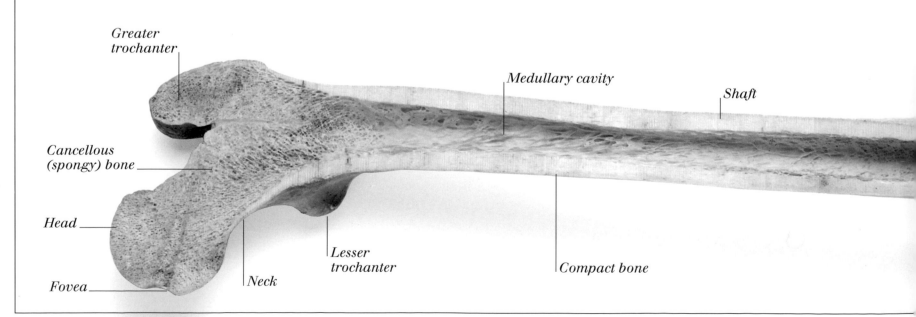

Greater trochanter

Medullary cavity

Shaft

Cancellous (spongy) bone

Head

Lesser trochanter

Compact bone

Fovea

Neck

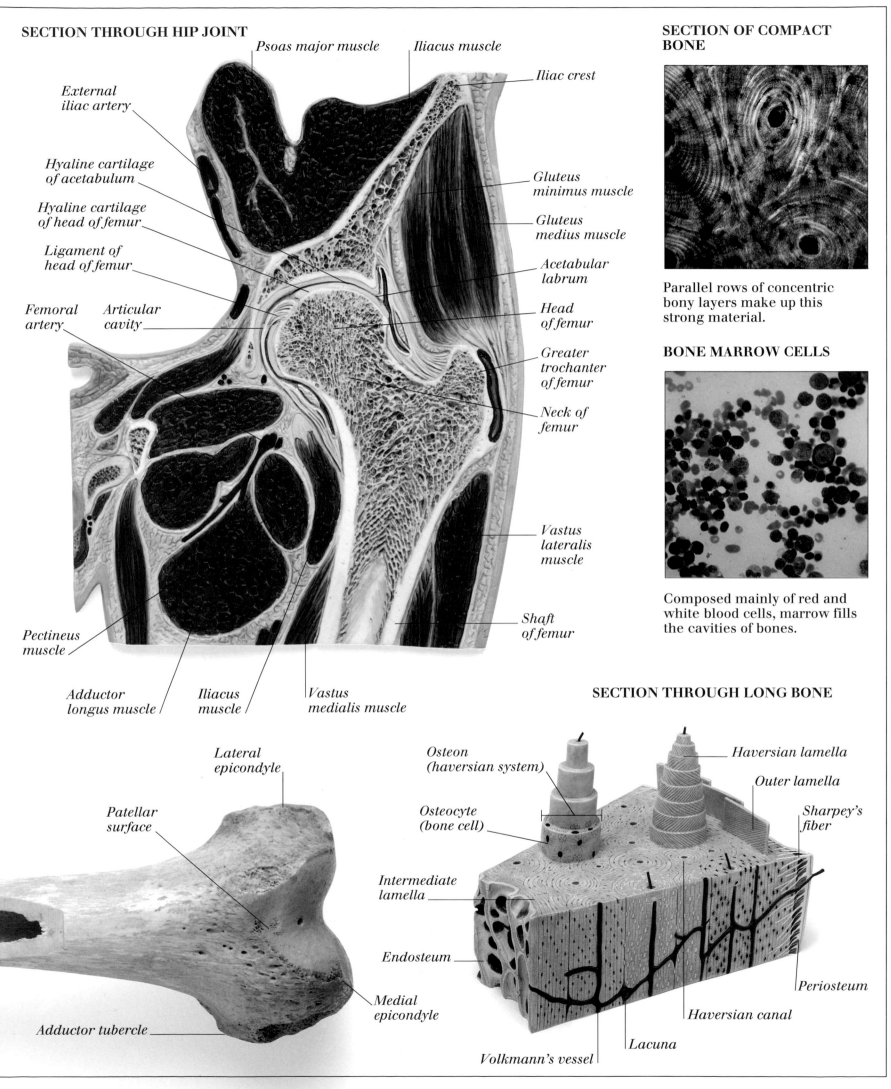

SECTION THROUGH HIP JOINT

Psoas major muscle

Iliacus muscle

Iliac crest

External iliac artery

Hyaline cartilage of acetabulum

Hyaline cartilage of head of femur

Ligament of head of femur

Femoral artery

Articular cavity

Gluteus minimus muscle

Gluteus medius muscle

Acetabular labrum

Head of femur

Greater trochanter of femur

Neck of femur

Vastus lateralis muscle

Shaft of femur

Pectineus muscle

Adductor longus muscle

Iliacus muscle

Vastus medialis muscle

SECTION OF COMPACT BONE

Parallel rows of concentric bony layers make up this strong material.

BONE MARROW CELLS

Composed mainly of red and white blood cells, marrow fills the cavities of bones.

SECTION THROUGH LONG BONE

Lateral epicondyle

Patellar surface

Adductor tubercle

Medial epicondyle

Osteon (haversian system)

Osteocyte (bone cell)

Intermediate lamella

Endosteum

Volkmann's vessel

Lacuna

Haversian canal

Haversian lamella

Outer lamella

Sharpey's fiber

Periosteum

Muscles 1

THERE ARE THREE MAIN TYPES OF MUSCLE: skeletal muscle (also called voluntary muscle because it can be consciously controlled); smooth muscle (also called involuntary muscle because it is not under voluntary control); and the specialized muscle tissue of the heart. Humans have more than 600 skeletal muscles, which differ in size and shape according to the jobs they do. Skeletal muscles are attached either directly or indirectly (via tendons) to bones, and work in opposing pairs (one muscle in the pair contracts while the other relaxes) to produce body movements as diverse as walking, threading a needle, and an array of facial expressions. Smooth muscles occur in the walls of internal body organs and perform actions such as forcing food through the intestines, contracting the uterus (womb) in childbirth, and pumping blood through the blood vessels.

SOME OTHER MUSCLES IN THE BODY

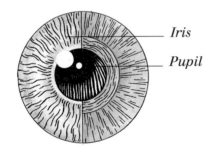

Iris

Pupil

IRIS
The muscle fibers contract and dilate (expand) to alter pupil size.

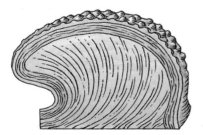

TONGUE
Interlacing layers of muscle allow great mobility.

ILEUM
Opposing muscle layers transport semidigested food.

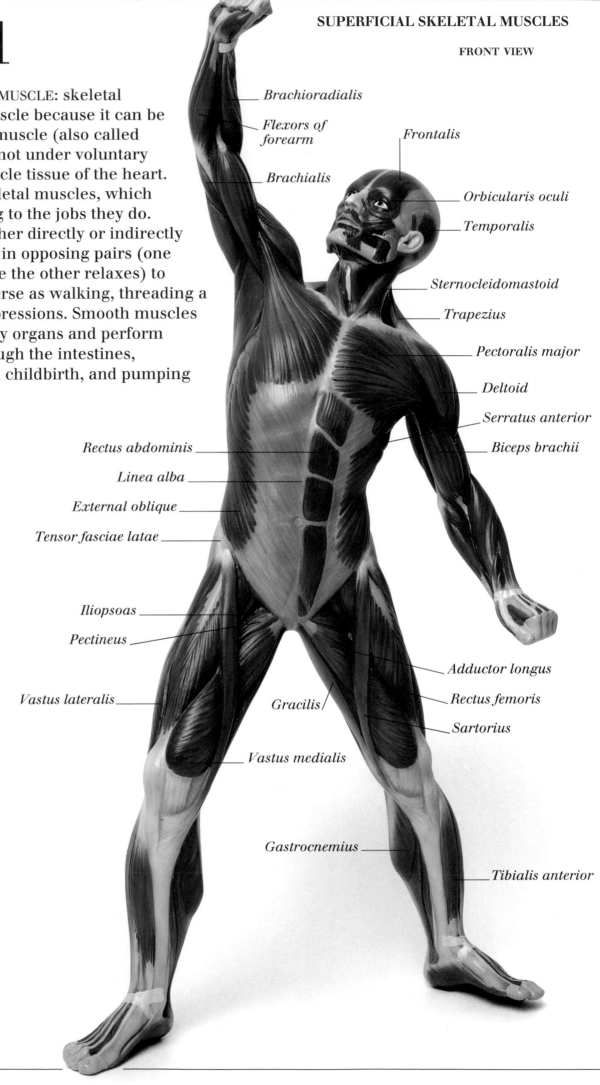

SUPERFICIAL SKELETAL MUSCLES

FRONT VIEW

Brachioradialis

Flexors of forearm

Brachialis

Frontalis

Orbicularis oculi

Temporalis

Sternocleidomastoid

Trapezius

Pectoralis major

Deltoid

Serratus anterior

Biceps brachii

Rectus abdominis

Linea alba

External oblique

Tensor fasciae latae

Iliopsoas

Pectineus

Adductor longus

Vastus lateralis

Gracilis

Rectus femoris

Sartorius

Vastus medialis

Gastrocnemius

Tibialis anterior

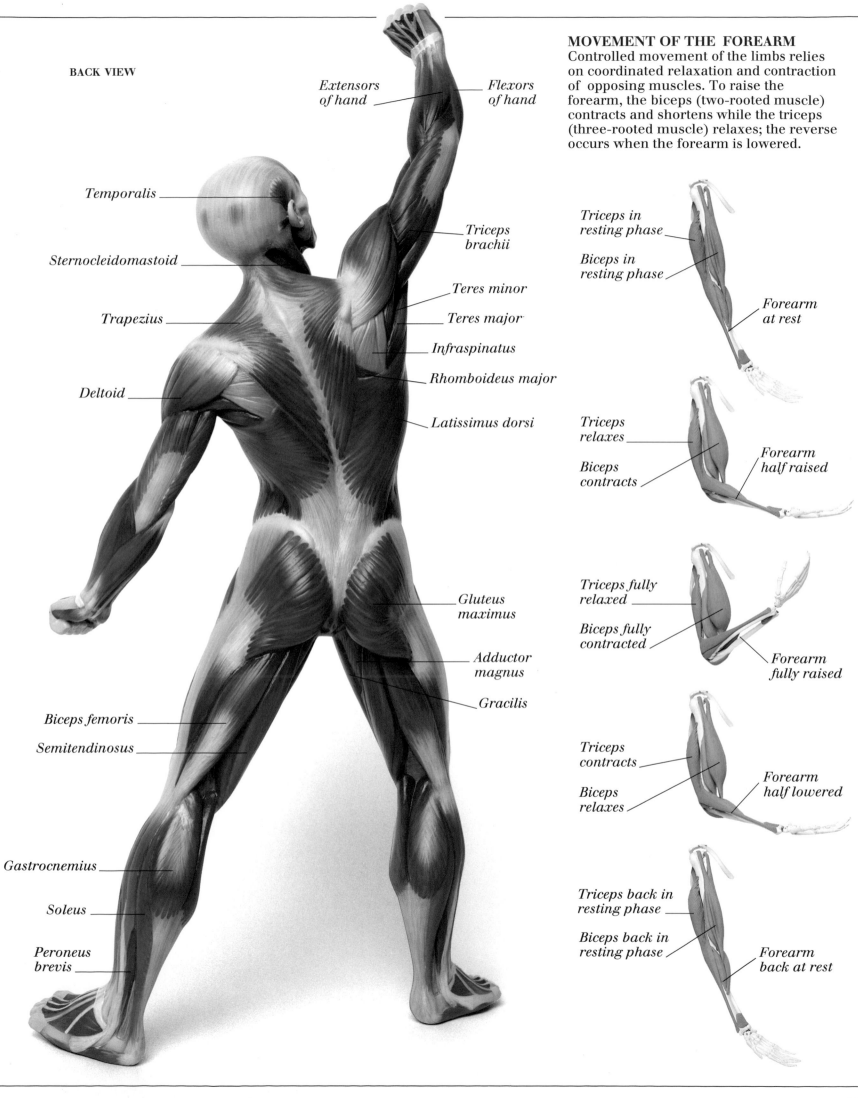

BACK VIEW

Extensors of hand

Flexors of hand

Temporalis

Sternocleidomastoid

Trapezius

Deltoid

Triceps brachii

Teres minor

Teres major

Infraspinatus

Rhomboideus major

Latissimus dorsi

Gluteus maximus

Adductor magnus

Gracilis

Biceps femoris

Semitendinosus

Gastrocnemius

Soleus

Peroneus brevis

MOVEMENT OF THE FOREARM
Controlled movement of the limbs relies on coordinated relaxation and contraction of opposing muscles. To raise the forearm, the biceps (two-rooted muscle) contracts and shortens while the triceps (three-rooted muscle) relaxes; the reverse occurs when the forearm is lowered.

Triceps in resting phase

Biceps in resting phase

Forearm at rest

Triceps relaxes

Biceps contracts

Forearm half raised

Triceps fully relaxed

Biceps fully contracted

Forearm fully raised

Triceps contracts

Biceps relaxes

Forearm half lowered

Triceps back in resting phase

Biceps back in resting phase

Forearm back at rest

23

Muscles 2

SKELETAL MUSCLE FIBER

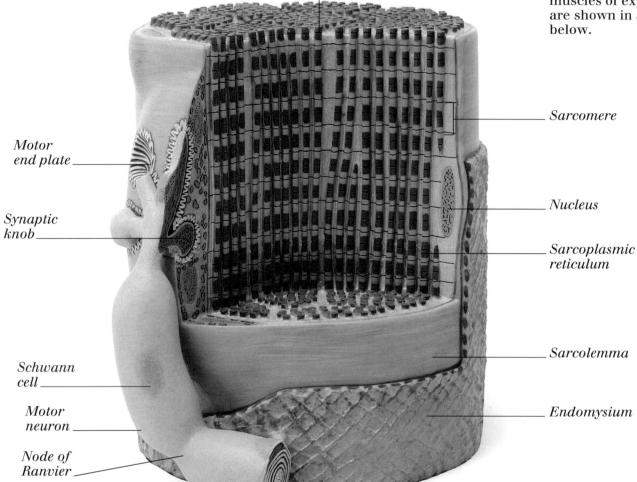

Myofibril

Sarcomere

Nucleus

Sarcoplasmic reticulum

Sarcolemma

Endomysium

Motor end plate

Synaptic knob

Schwann cell

Motor neuron

Node of Ranvier

MUSCLES OF FACIAL EXPRESSION
A single expression is the result of movement of many muscles; the main muscles of expression are shown in action below.

FRONTALIS

CORRUGATOR SUPERCILII

ORBICULARIS ORIS

ZYGOMATICUS MAJOR

DEPRESSOR ANGULI ORIS

TYPES OF MUSCLE

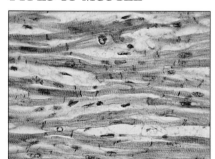

CARDIAC MUSCLE

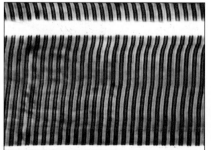

SKELETAL MUSCLE

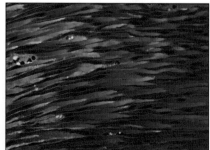

SMOOTH MUSCLE

CONTRACTION OF SKELETAL MUSCLE

RELAXED STATE

CONTRACTED STATE

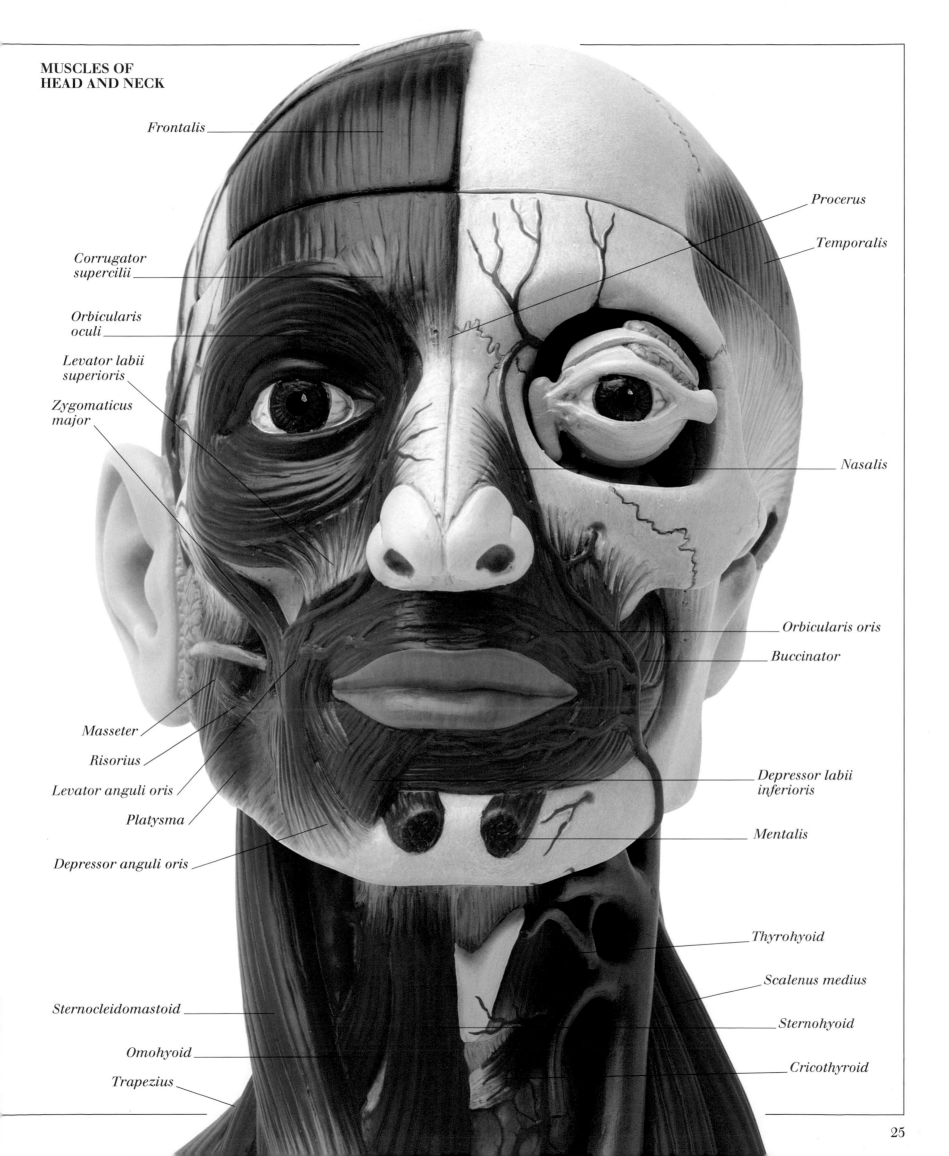

MUSCLES OF HEAD AND NECK

Frontalis

Corrugator supercilii

Orbicularis oculi

Levator labii superioris

Zygomaticus major

Masseter

Risorius

Levator anguli oris

Platysma

Depressor anguli oris

Sternocleidomastoid

Omohyoid

Trapezius

Procerus

Temporalis

Nasalis

Orbicularis oris

Buccinator

Depressor labii inferioris

Mentalis

Thyrohyoid

Scalenus medius

Sternohyoid

Cricothyroid

Hands

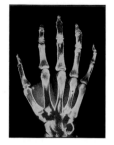

THE HUMAN HAND is an extremely versatile tool, capable of delicate manipulation as well as powerful gripping actions. The arrangement of its 27 small bones, moved by 37 skeletal muscles that are connected to the bones by tendons, allows a wide range of movements. In particular, it is our ability to bring the tips of our thumbs and fingers together, combined with the extraordinary sensitivity of our fingertips due to their rich supply of nerve endings, that gives human hands their unique dexterity.

BONES OF HAND

Ring finger

Middle finger

Index finger

Little finger

Distal phalanx

Middle phalanx

Proximal phalanx

2nd metacarpal

3rd metacarpal

4th metacarpal

5th metacarpal

Hamate

Pisiform

Capitate

Triquetral

Lunate

Ulna

Head

Shaft

Base

Trapezium

Trapezoid

Scaphoid

Radius

Distal phalanx of thumb

Proximal phalanx of thumb

1st metacarpal

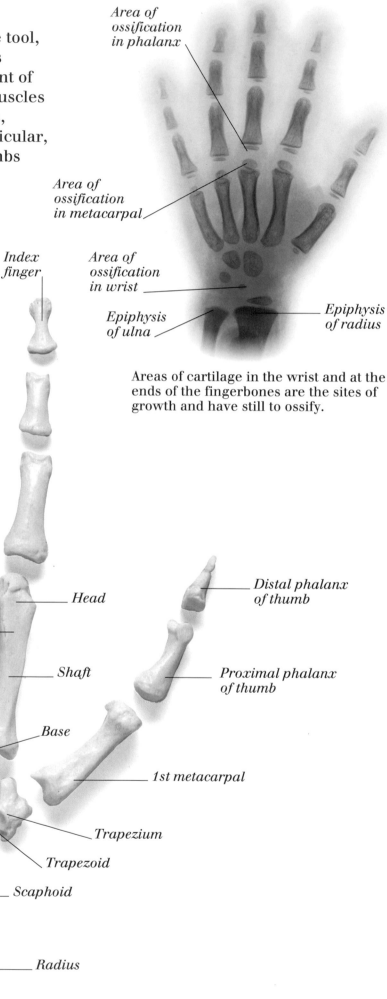

X-RAY OF LEFT HAND OF A YOUNG CHILD

Area of ossification in phalanx

Area of ossification in metacarpal

Area of ossification in wrist

Epiphysis of ulna

Epiphysis of radius

Areas of cartilage in the wrist and at the ends of the fingerbones are the sites of growth and have still to ossify.

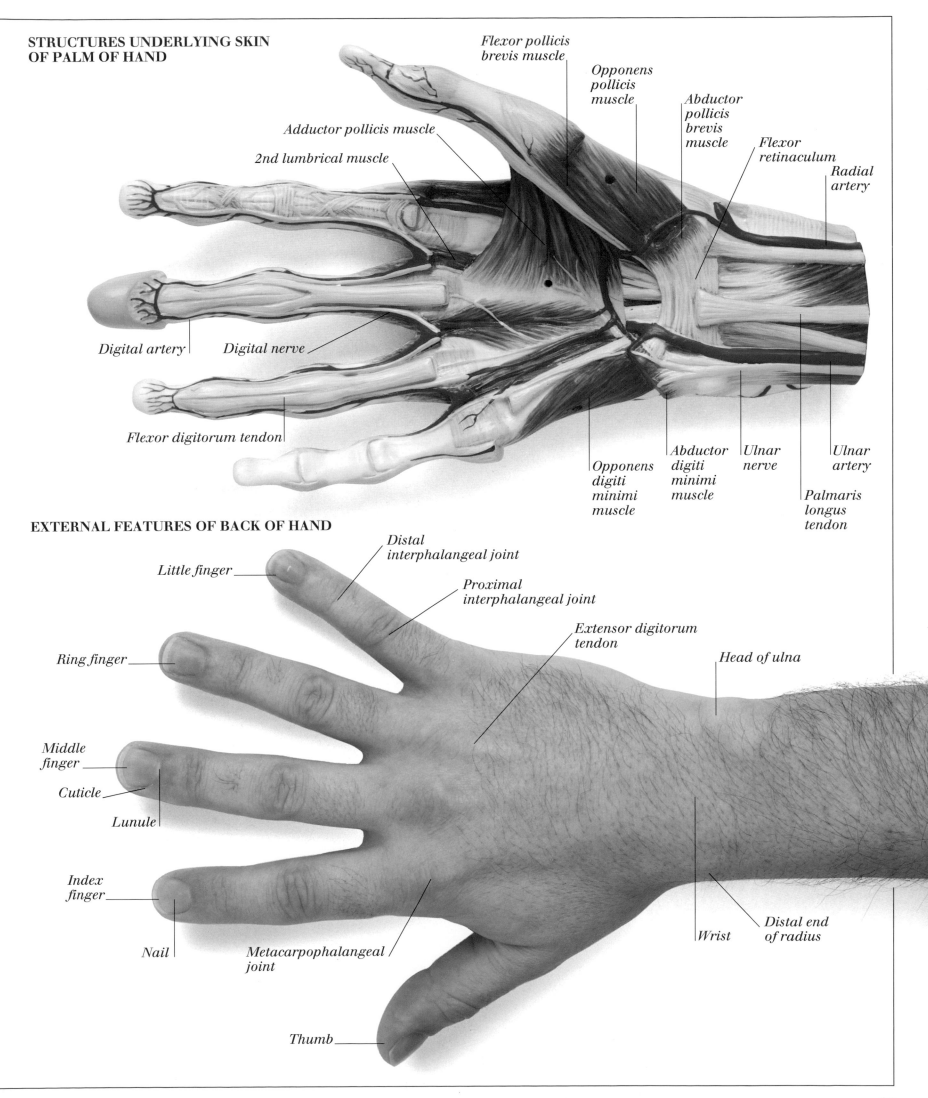

STRUCTURES UNDERLYING SKIN OF PALM OF HAND

Flexor pollicis brevis muscle

Opponens pollicis muscle

Abductor pollicis brevis muscle

Flexor retinaculum

Radial artery

Adductor pollicis muscle

2nd lumbrical muscle

Digital artery

Digital nerve

Flexor digitorum tendon

Opponens digiti minimi muscle

Abductor digiti minimi muscle

Ulnar nerve

Ulnar artery

Palmaris longus tendon

EXTERNAL FEATURES OF BACK OF HAND

Distal interphalangeal joint

Little finger

Proximal interphalangeal joint

Extensor digitorum tendon

Head of ulna

Ring finger

Middle finger

Cuticle

Lunule

Index finger

Nail

Metacarpophalangeal joint

Wrist

Distal end of radius

Thumb

Feet

THE FEET AND TOES are essential elements in body movement. They bear and propel the weight of the body during walking and running, and also help to maintain balance during changes of body position. Each foot has 26 bones, more than 100 ligaments, and 33 muscles, some of which are attached to the lower leg. The heel pad and the arch of the foot act as shock absorbers, providing a cushion against the jolts that occur with every step.

BONES OF FOOT

LIGAMENTS OF FOOT

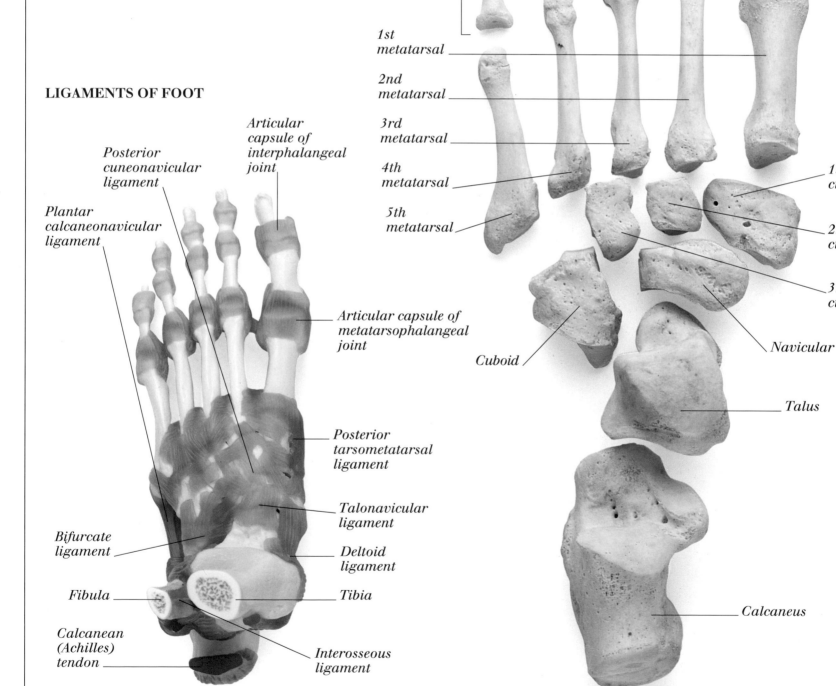

- 2nd toe
- Hallux (big toe)
- 3rd toe
- Distal phalanx of hallux
- 4th toe
- Proximal phalanx of hallux
- 5th (little) toe
- Distal phalanx
- Middle phalanx
- Proximal phalanx
- 1st metatarsal
- 2nd metatarsal
- 3rd metatarsal
- 4th metatarsal
- 5th metatarsal
- 1st cuneiform
- 2nd cuneiform
- 3rd cuneiform
- Navicular
- Cuboid
- Talus
- Calcaneus

- Posterior cuneonavicular ligament
- Articular capsule of interphalangeal joint
- Plantar calcaneonavicular ligament
- Articular capsule of metatarsophalangeal joint
- Posterior tarsometatarsal ligament
- Talonavicular ligament
- Bifurcate ligament
- Deltoid ligament
- Fibula
- Tibia
- Calcanean (Achilles) tendon
- Interosseous ligament

STRUCTURES UNDERLYING SKIN OF FOOT

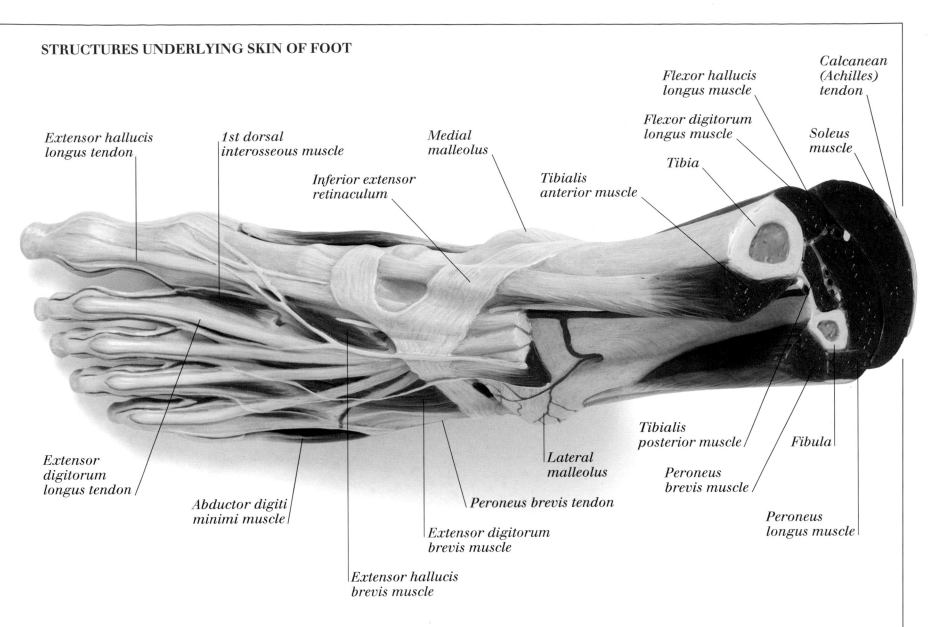

Extensor hallucis longus tendon

1st dorsal interosseous muscle

Inferior extensor retinaculum

Medial malleolus

Tibialis anterior muscle

Flexor hallucis longus muscle

Flexor digitorum longus muscle

Tibia

Soleus muscle

Calcanean (Achilles) tendon

Extensor digitorum longus tendon

Abductor digiti minimi muscle

Extensor hallucis brevis muscle

Extensor digitorum brevis muscle

Peroneus brevis tendon

Lateral malleolus

Tibialis posterior muscle

Peroneus brevis muscle

Fibula

Peroneus longus muscle

EXTERNAL FEATURES OF FOOT

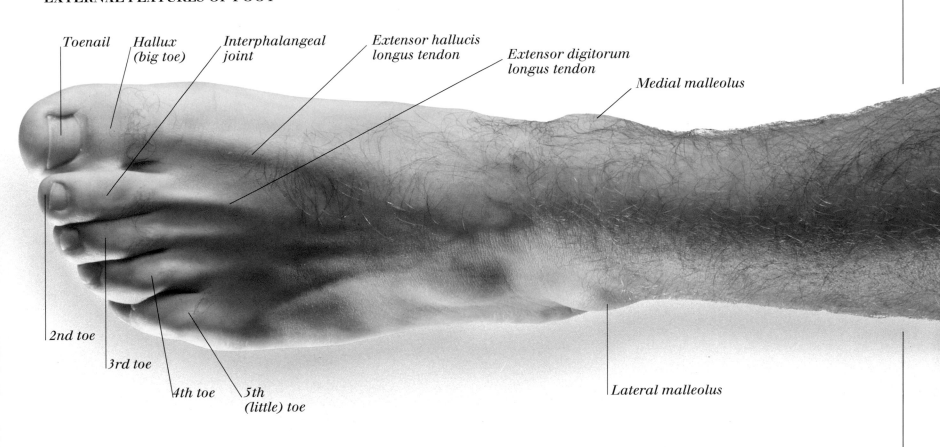

Toenail

Hallux (big toe)

Interphalangeal joint

Extensor hallucis longus tendon

Extensor digitorum longus tendon

Medial malleolus

2nd toe

3rd toe

4th toe

5th (little) toe

Lateral malleolus

Skin and hair

SKIN IS THE BODY'S LARGEST ORGAN, a waterproof barrier that protects the internal organs against infection, injury, and harmful sun rays. The skin is also an important sensory organ and helps to control body temperature. The outer layer of the skin, known as the epidermis, is coated with keratin, a tough, horny protein that is also the chief consistituent of hair and nails. Dead cells are shed from the skin's surface and are replaced by new cells from the base of the epidermis, the region that also produces the skin pigment, melanin. The dermis contains most of the skin's living structures, and includes nerve endings, blood vessels, elastic fibers, sweat glands that cool the skin, and sebaceous glands that produce oil to keep the skin supple. Beneath the dermis lies the subcutaneous tissue (hypodermis), which is rich in fat and blood vessels. Hair shafts grow from hair follicles situated in the dermis and subcutaneous tissue. Hair grows on every part of the skin apart from the palms of the hands and soles of the feet.

SECTION OF HAIR

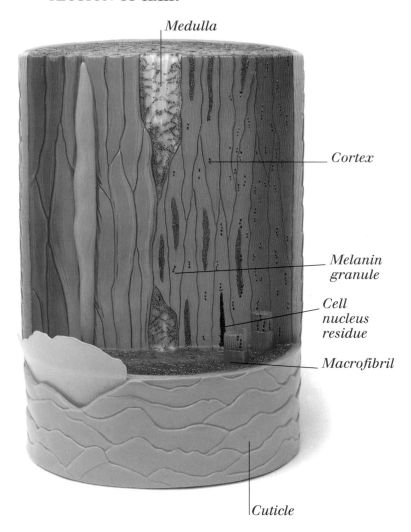

Medulla

Cortex

Melanin granule

Cell nucleus residue

Macrofibril

Cuticle

SECTIONS OF DIFFERENT TYPES OF SKIN

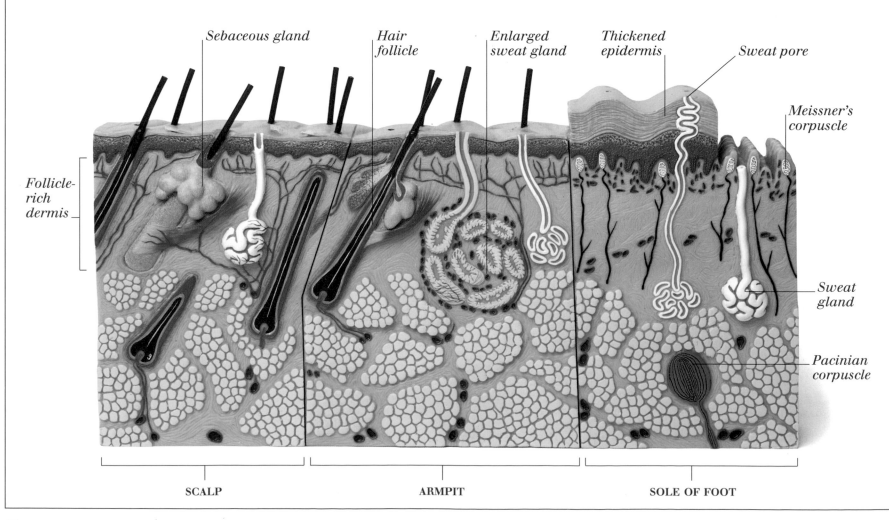

Sebaceous gland

Hair follicle

Enlarged sweat gland

Thickened epidermis

Sweat pore

Meissner's corpuscle

Follicle-rich dermis

Sweat gland

Pacinian corpuscle

SCALP

ARMPIT

SOLE OF FOOT

SECTION OF SKIN

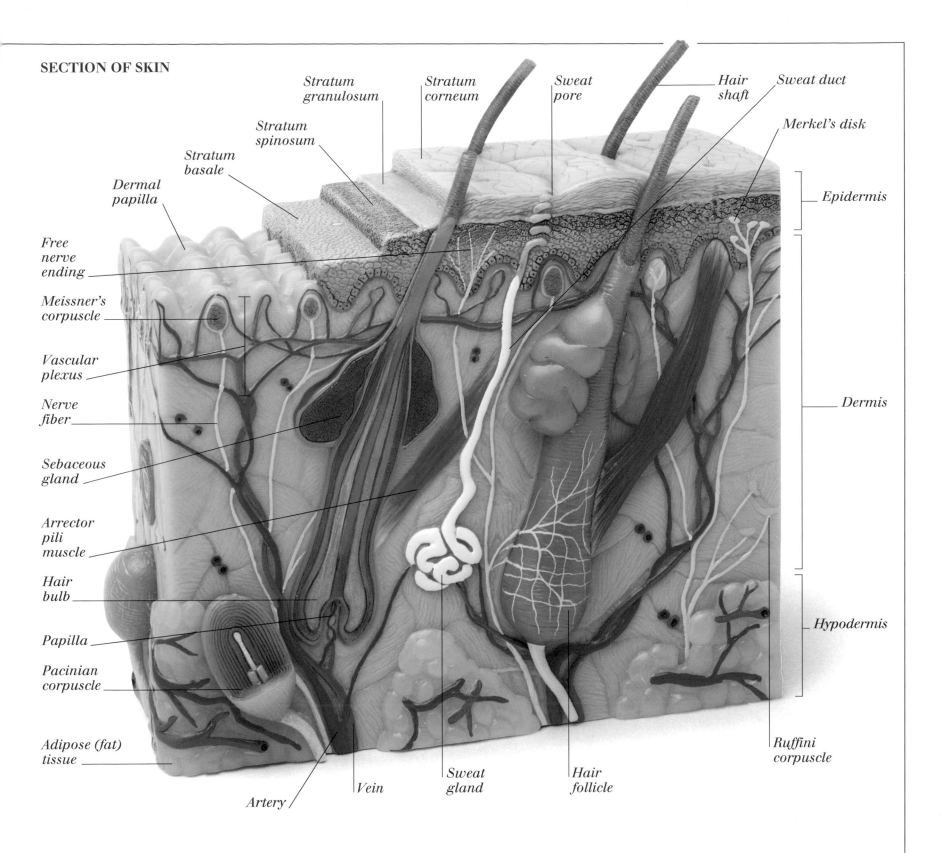

Stratum granulosum

Stratum corneum

Sweat pore

Hair shaft

Sweat duct

Stratum spinosum

Merkel's disk

Stratum basale

Epidermis

Dermal papilla

Free nerve ending

Meissner's corpuscle

Vascular plexus

Nerve fiber

Sebaceous gland

Arrector pili muscle

Hair bulb

Papilla

Pacinian corpuscle

Adipose (fat) tissue

Artery

Vein

Sweat gland

Hair follicle

Dermis

Hypodermis

Ruffini corpuscle

PHOTOMICROGRAPHS OF SKIN AND HAIR

SECTION OF SKIN
The flaky cells at the skin's surface are shed continuously.

SWEAT PORE
This allows loss of fluid as part of temperature control.

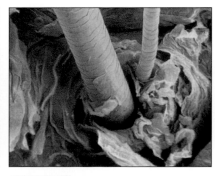

SKIN HAIR
Two hairs pushing through the outer layer of skin.

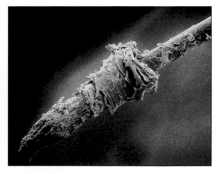

HEAD HAIR
The root and part of the shaft of a hair from the scalp.

31

Brain

THE BRAIN IS THE MAJOR ORGAN of the central nervous system and the control center for all the body's voluntary and involuntary activities. It is also responsible for the complexities of thought, memory, emotion, and language. In adults, this complex organ is a mere 3 lb (1.4 kg) in weight, containing over 10 thousand million nerve cells. Three distinct regions can easily be seen—the brainstem, the cerebellum, and the large cerebrum. The brainstem controls vital body functions, such as breathing and digestion. The cerebellum's main functions are the maintenance of posture and the coordination of body movements. The cerebrum, which consists of the right and left cerebral hemispheres joined by the corpus callosum, is the site of most conscious and intelligent activities.

MRI SCAN OF TRANSVERSE SECTION THROUGH BRAIN

White matter

Skull

Scalp

Gray matter

Lateral ventricle

Longitudinal fissure

Coronal section

Sagittal section

SAGITTAL SECTION THROUGH BRAIN

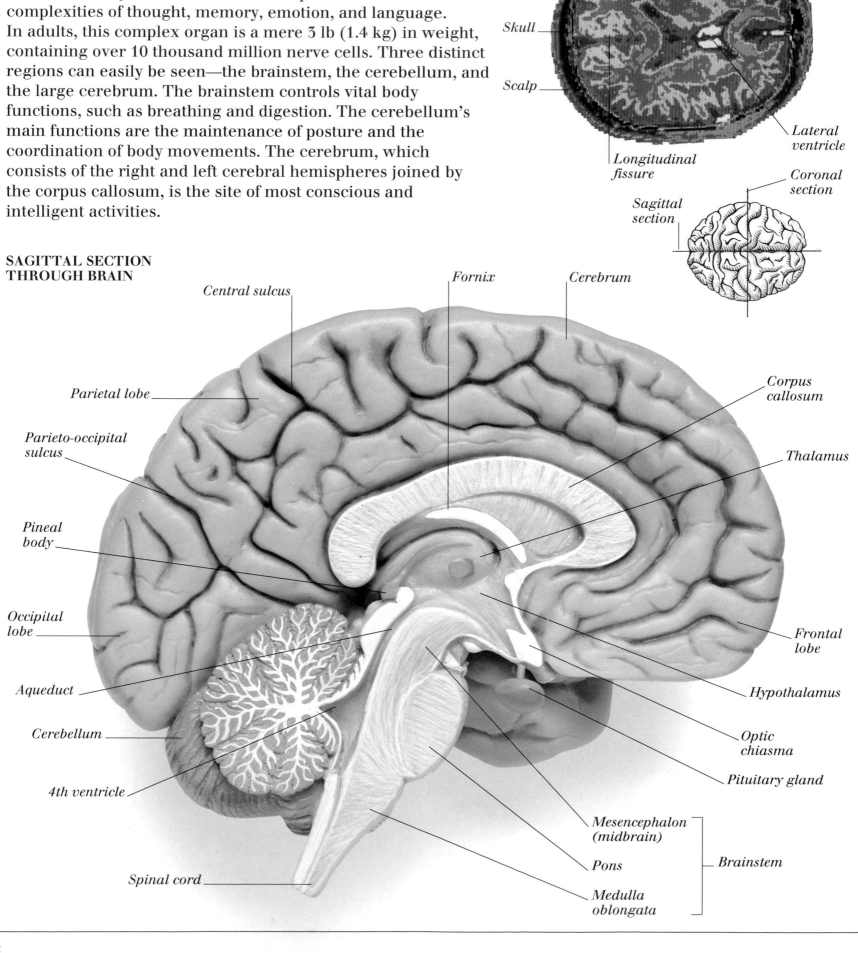

Central sulcus

Fornix

Cerebrum

Parietal lobe

Corpus callosum

Parieto-occipital sulcus

Thalamus

Pineal body

Occipital lobe

Frontal lobe

Aqueduct

Hypothalamus

Cerebellum

Optic chiasma

4th ventricle

Pituitary gland

Spinal cord

Mesencephalon (midbrain)

Pons

Brainstem

Medulla oblongata

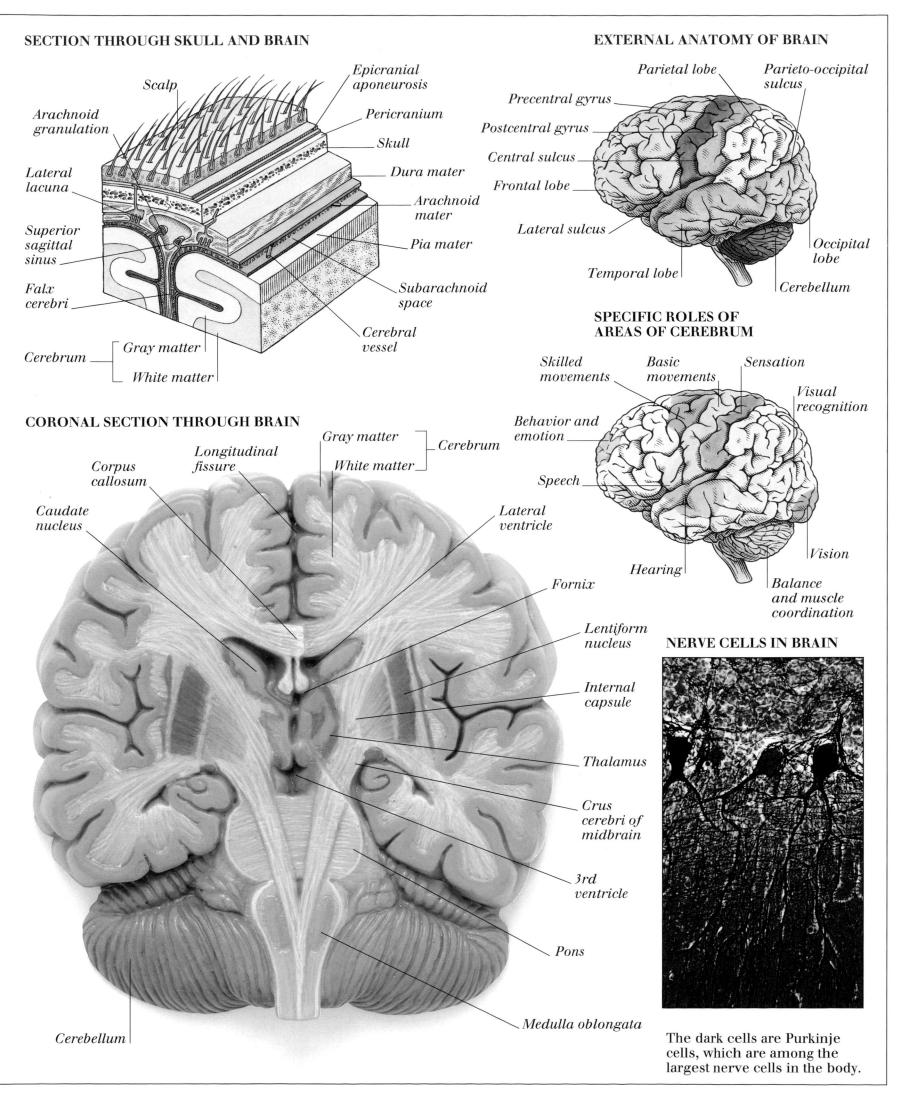

SECTION THROUGH SKULL AND BRAIN

Scalp

Epicranial aponeurosis

Arachnoid granulation

Pericranium

Skull

Lateral lacuna

Dura mater

Superior sagittal sinus

Arachnoid mater

Pia mater

Falx cerebri

Subarachnoid space

Cerebral vessel

Cerebrum { Gray matter / White matter }

EXTERNAL ANATOMY OF BRAIN

Parietal lobe

Parieto-occipital sulcus

Precentral gyrus

Postcentral gyrus

Central sulcus

Frontal lobe

Lateral sulcus

Occipital lobe

Temporal lobe

Cerebellum

SPECIFIC ROLES OF AREAS OF CEREBRUM

Skilled movements

Basic movements

Sensation

Visual recognition

Behavior and emotion

Speech

Hearing

Vision

Balance and muscle coordination

CORONAL SECTION THROUGH BRAIN

Corpus callosum

Longitudinal fissure

Gray matter

White matter

Cerebrum

Caudate nucleus

Lateral ventricle

Fornix

Lentiform nucleus

Internal capsule

Thalamus

Crus cerebri of midbrain

3rd ventricle

Pons

Medulla oblongata

Cerebellum

NERVE CELLS IN BRAIN

The dark cells are Purkinje cells, which are among the largest nerve cells in the body.

33

Nervous system

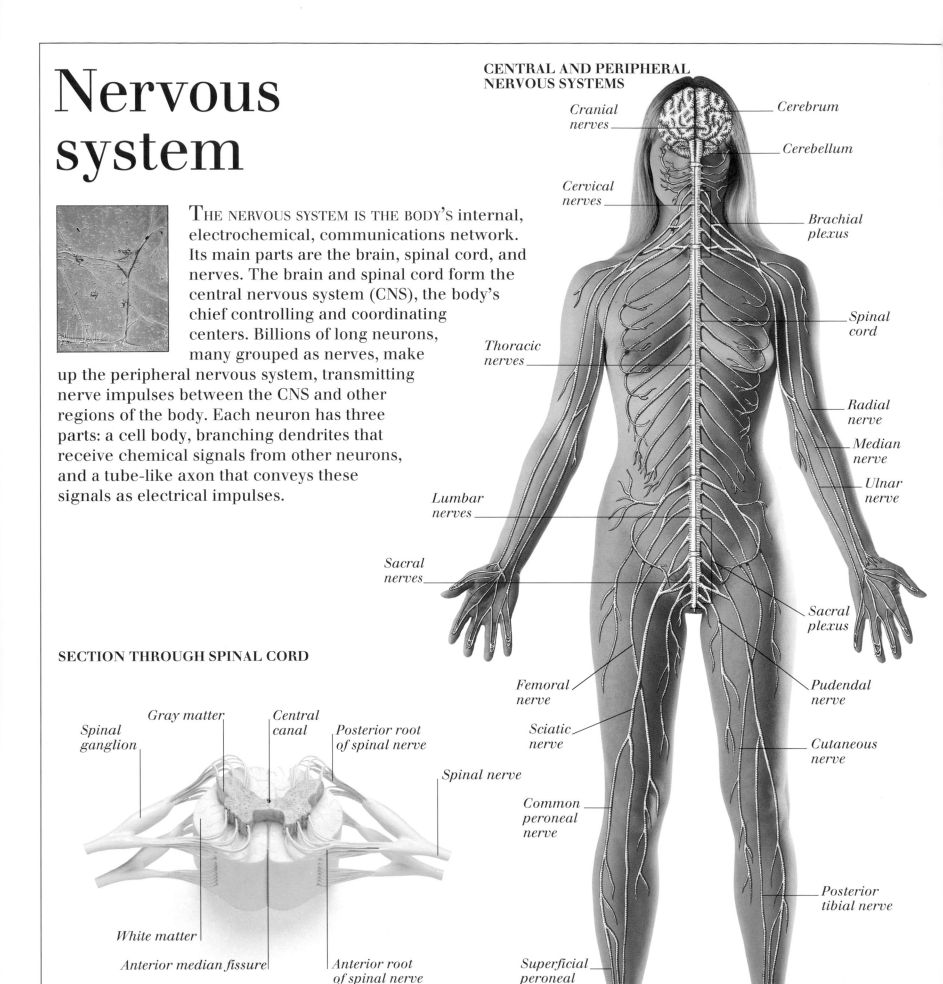

THE NERVOUS SYSTEM IS THE BODY'S internal, electrochemical, communications network. Its main parts are the brain, spinal cord, and nerves. The brain and spinal cord form the central nervous system (CNS), the body's chief controlling and coordinating centers. Billions of long neurons, many grouped as nerves, make up the peripheral nervous system, transmitting nerve impulses between the CNS and other regions of the body. Each neuron has three parts: a cell body, branching dendrites that receive chemical signals from other neurons, and a tube-like axon that conveys these signals as electrical impulses.

CENTRAL AND PERIPHERAL NERVOUS SYSTEMS

Cranial nerves

Cerebrum

Cerebellum

Cervical nerves

Brachial plexus

Thoracic nerves

Spinal cord

Radial nerve

Median nerve

Ulnar nerve

Lumbar nerves

Sacral nerves

Sacral plexus

Femoral nerve

Pudendal nerve

Sciatic nerve

Cutaneous nerve

Common peroneal nerve

Posterior tibial nerve

Superficial peroneal nerve

Deep peroneal nerve

SECTION THROUGH SPINAL CORD

Spinal ganglion

Gray matter

Central canal

Posterior root of spinal nerve

Spinal nerve

White matter

Anterior median fissure

Anterior root of spinal nerve

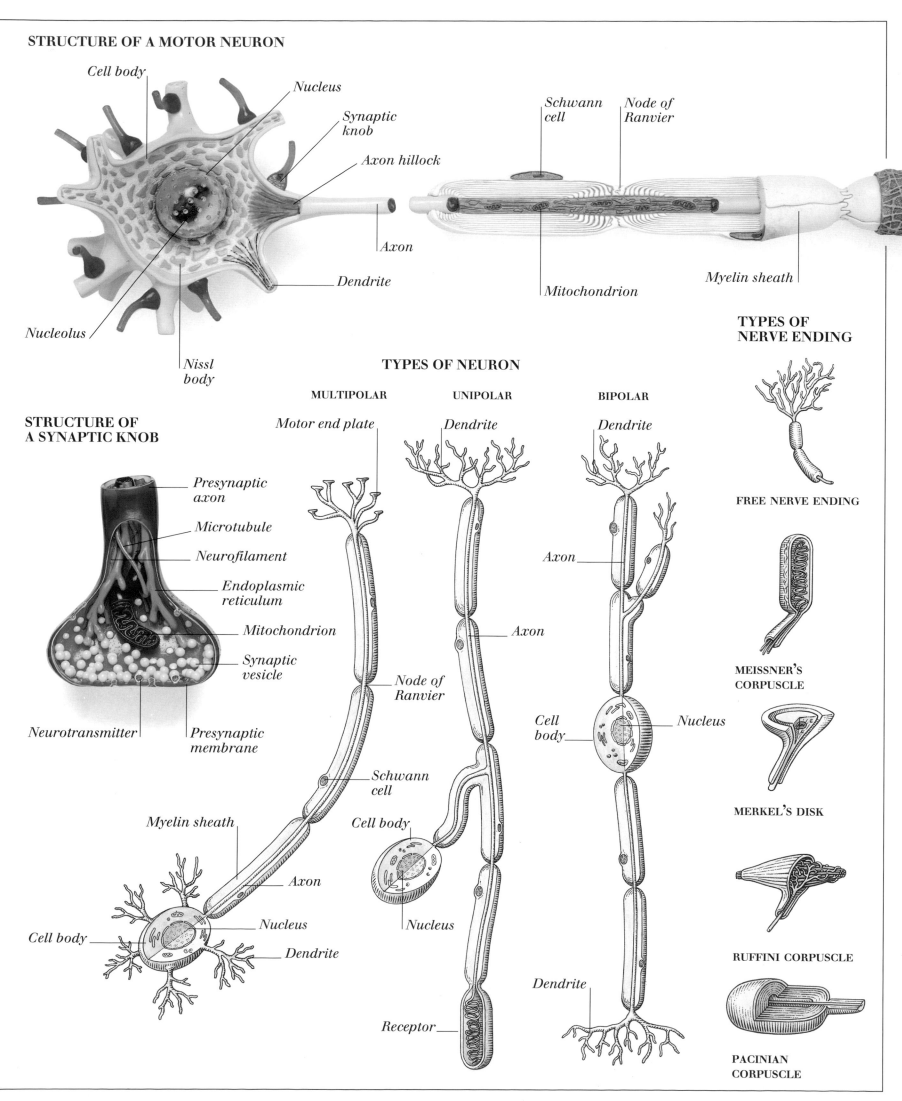

STRUCTURE OF A MOTOR NEURON

Cell body

Nucleus

Synaptic knob

Axon hillock

Axon

Dendrite

Nucleolus

Nissl body

Schwann cell

Node of Ranvier

Mitochondrion

Myelin sheath

TYPES OF NERVE ENDING

FREE NERVE ENDING

MEISSNER'S CORPUSCLE

MERKEL'S DISK

RUFFINI CORPUSCLE

PACINIAN CORPUSCLE

TYPES OF NEURON

MULTIPOLAR

Motor end plate

Node of Ranvier

Schwann cell

Myelin sheath

Axon

Cell body

Nucleus

Dendrite

UNIPOLAR

Dendrite

Axon

Cell body

Nucleus

Receptor

BIPOLAR

Dendrite

Axon

Cell body

Nucleus

Dendrite

STRUCTURE OF A SYNAPTIC KNOB

Presynaptic axon

Microtubule

Neurofilament

Endoplasmic reticulum

Mitochondrion

Synaptic vesicle

Neurotransmitter

Presynaptic membrane

Eye

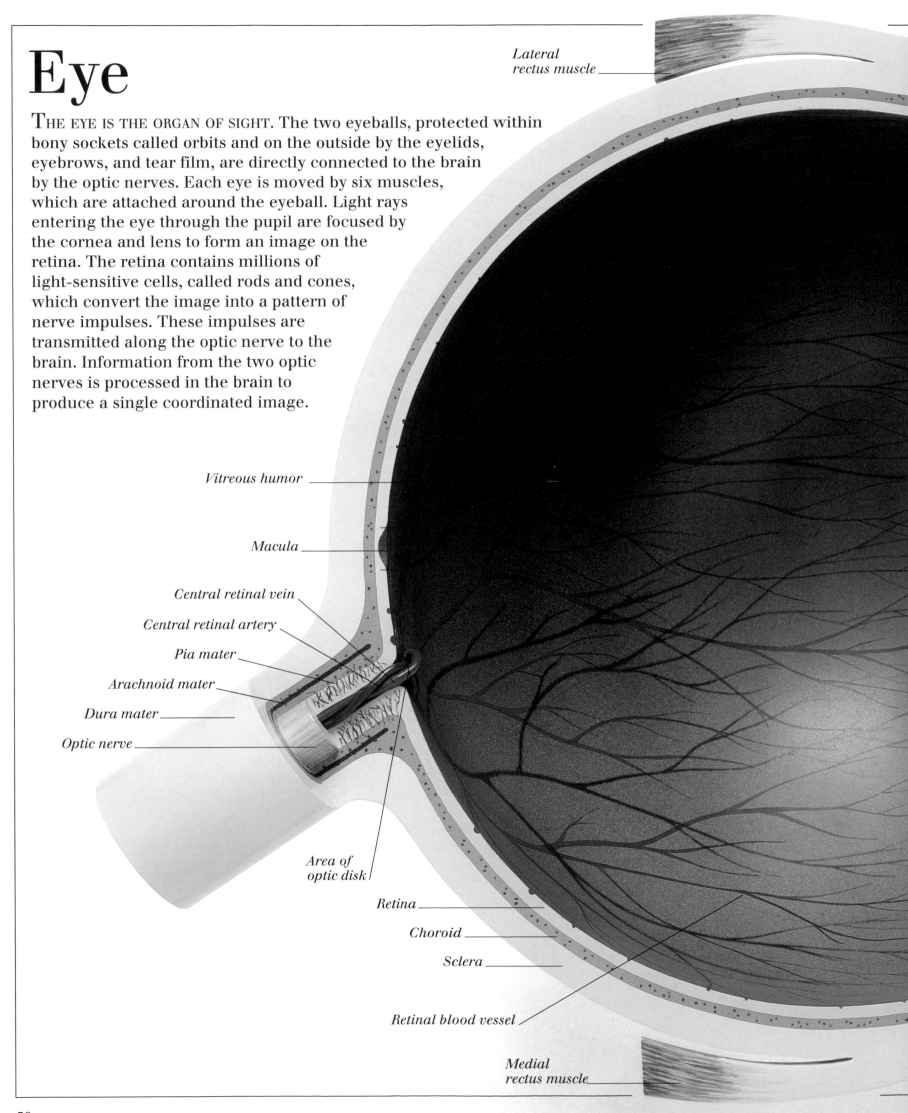

THE EYE IS THE ORGAN OF SIGHT. The two eyeballs, protected within bony sockets called orbits and on the outside by the eyelids, eyebrows, and tear film, are directly connected to the brain by the optic nerves. Each eye is moved by six muscles, which are attached around the eyeball. Light rays entering the eye through the pupil are focused by the cornea and lens to form an image on the retina. The retina contains millions of light-sensitive cells, called rods and cones, which convert the image into a pattern of nerve impulses. These impulses are transmitted along the optic nerve to the brain. Information from the two optic nerves is processed in the brain to produce a single coordinated image.

Lateral rectus muscle

Vitreous humor

Macula

Central retinal vein

Central retinal artery

Pia mater

Arachnoid mater

Dura mater

Optic nerve

Area of optic disk

Retina

Choroid

Sclera

Retinal blood vessel

Medial rectus muscle

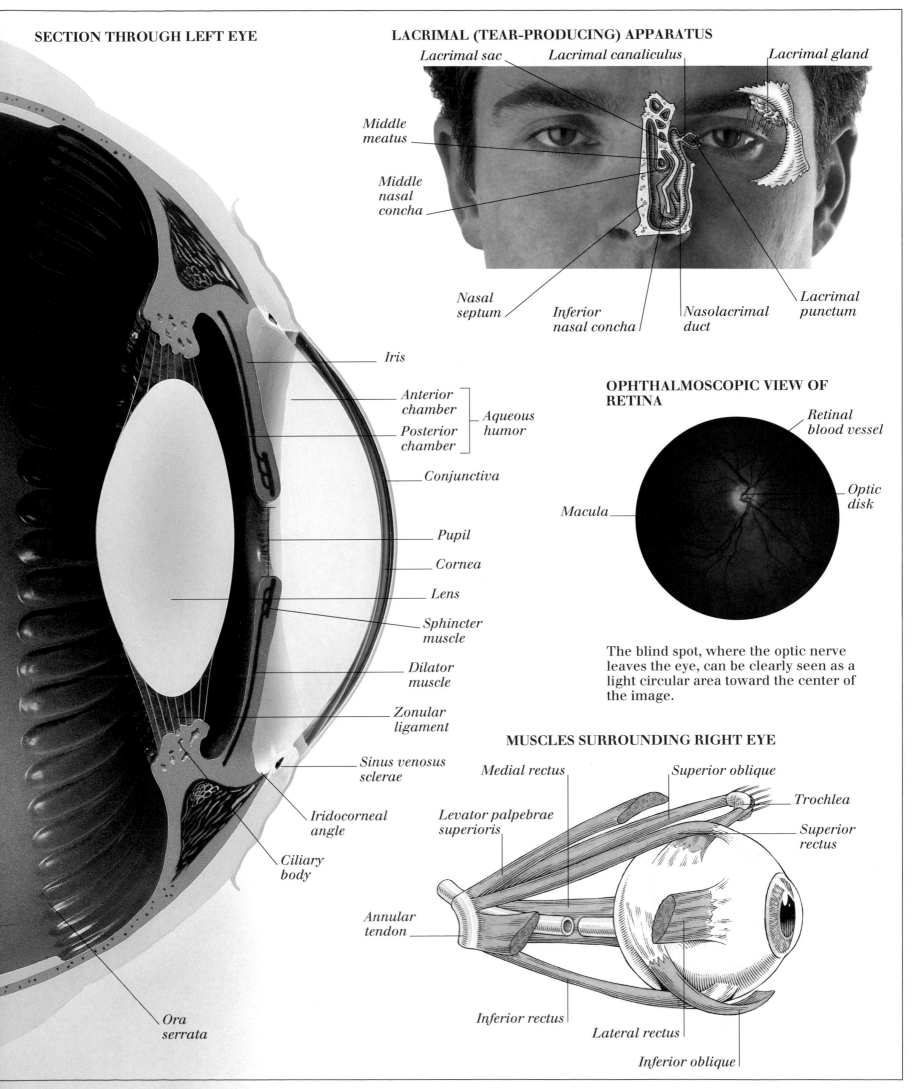

SECTION THROUGH LEFT EYE

Iris

Anterior chamber

Posterior chamber

Aqueous humor

Conjunctiva

Pupil

Cornea

Lens

Sphincter muscle

Dilator muscle

Zonular ligament

Sinus venosus sclerae

Iridocorneal angle

Ciliary body

Ora serrata

LACRIMAL (TEAR-PRODUCING) APPARATUS

Lacrimal sac

Lacrimal canaliculus

Lacrimal gland

Middle meatus

Middle nasal concha

Nasal septum

Inferior nasal concha

Nasolacrimal duct

Lacrimal punctum

OPHTHALMOSCOPIC VIEW OF RETINA

Retinal blood vessel

Optic disk

Macula

The blind spot, where the optic nerve leaves the eye, can be clearly seen as a light circular area toward the center of the image.

MUSCLES SURROUNDING RIGHT EYE

Medial rectus

Superior oblique

Levator palpebrae superioris

Trochlea

Superior rectus

Annular tendon

Inferior rectus

Lateral rectus

Inferior oblique

37

Ear

THE EAR IS THE ORGAN OF HEARING AND BALANCE. The outer ear consists of a flap called the auricle or pinna and the auditory canal. The main functional parts—the middle and inner ears—are enclosed within the skull. The middle ear consists of three tiny bones, known as auditory ossicles, and the eustachian tube, which links the ear to the back of the nose. The inner ear consists of the spiral-shaped cochlea, and also the semicircular canals and the vestibule, which are the organs of balance. Sound waves entering the ear travel through the auditory canal to the tympanic membrane (eardrum), where they are converted to vibrations that are transmitted via the ossicles to the cochlea. Here, the vibrations are converted by millions of microscopic hairs into electrical nerve signals to be interpreted by the brain.

STRUCTURE OF EAR

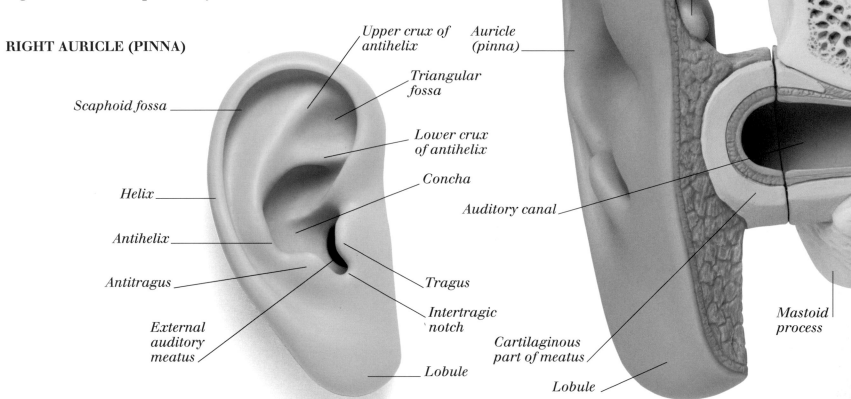

Temporal bone

Cartilage of auricle

Auricle (pinna)

Auditory canal

Mastoid process

Cartilaginous part of meatus

Lobule

RIGHT AURICLE (PINNA)

Upper crux of antihelix

Triangular fossa

Lower crux of antihelix

Scaphoid fossa

Concha

Helix

Antihelix

Antitragus

Tragus

Intertragic notch

External auditory meatus

Lobule

OSSICLES OF MIDDLE EAR

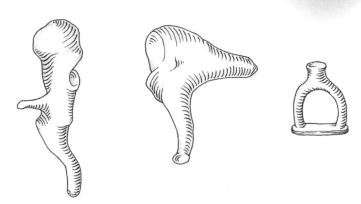

MALLEUS (HAMMER)   INCUS (ANVIL)   STAPES (STIRRUP)

These three tiny bones connect to form a bridge between the tympanic membrane and the oval window. With a system of membranes they convey sound vibrations to the inner ear.

INTERNAL STRUCTURE OF AMPULLA

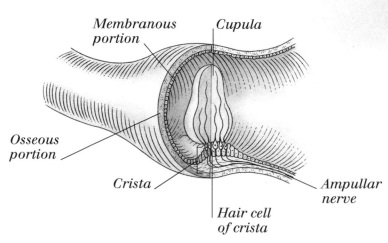

Membranous portion

Cupula

Osseous portion

Crista

Hair cell of crista

Ampullar nerve

LABYRINTH

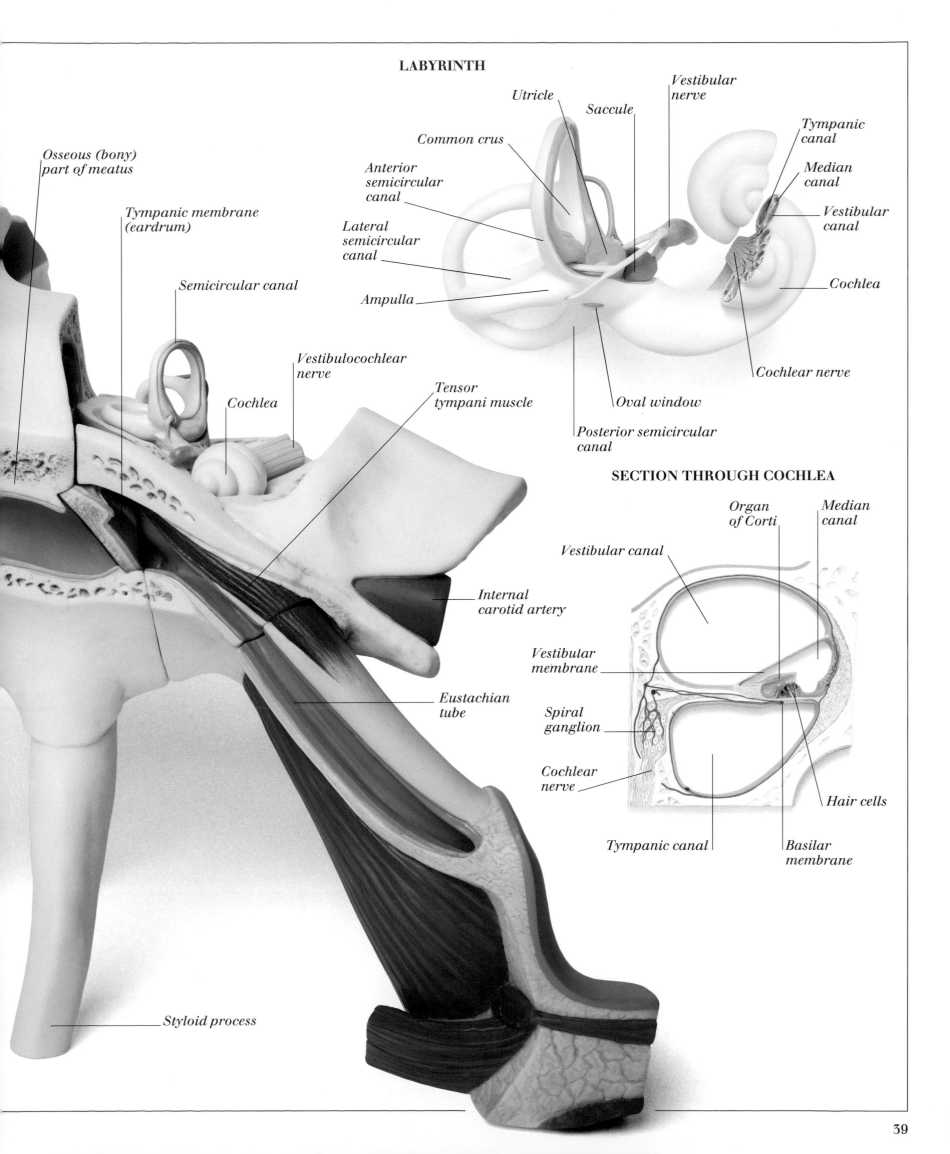

Osseous (bony) part of meatus

Tympanic membrane (eardrum)

Semicircular canal

Vestibulocochlear nerve

Cochlea

Tensor tympani muscle

Utricle

Common crus

Saccule

Vestibular nerve

Anterior semicircular canal

Lateral semicircular canal

Ampulla

Tympanic canal

Median canal

Vestibular canal

Cochlea

Cochlear nerve

Oval window

Posterior semicircular canal

Internal carotid artery

Eustachian tube

Styloid process

SECTION THROUGH COCHLEA

Organ of Corti

Median canal

Vestibular canal

Vestibular membrane

Spiral ganglion

Cochlear nerve

Tympanic canal

Hair cells

Basilar membrane

39

Nose, mouth, and throat

WITH EVERY BREATH, air passes through the nasal cavity down the pharynx (throat), larynx ("voice box"), and trachea (windpipe) to the lungs. The nasal cavity warms and moistens air, and the tiny layers in its lining protect the airway against damage by foreign bodies. During swallowing, the tongue moves up and back, the larynx rises, the epiglottis closes off the entrance to the trachea, and the soft palate separates the nasal cavity from the pharynx. Saliva, secreted from three pairs of salivary glands, lubricates food to make swallowing easier; it also begins the chemical breakdown of food, and helps to produce taste. The senses of taste and smell are closely linked. Both depend on the detection of dissolved molecules by sensory receptors in the olfactory nerve endings of the nose and in the taste buds of the tongue.

STRUCTURE OF TONGUE

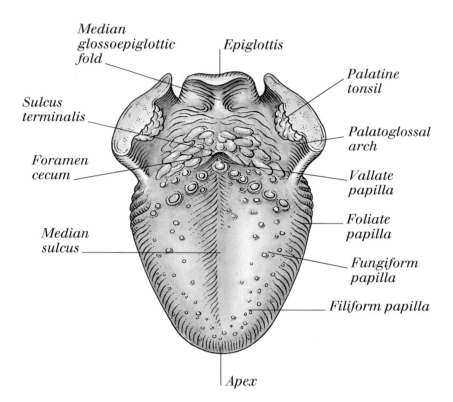

Median glossoepiglottic fold
Epiglottis
Sulcus terminalis
Palatine tonsil
Foramen cecum
Palatoglossal arch
Median sulcus
Vallate papilla
Foliate papilla
Fungiform papilla
Filiform papilla
Apex

STRUCTURES SURROUNDING PHARYNX

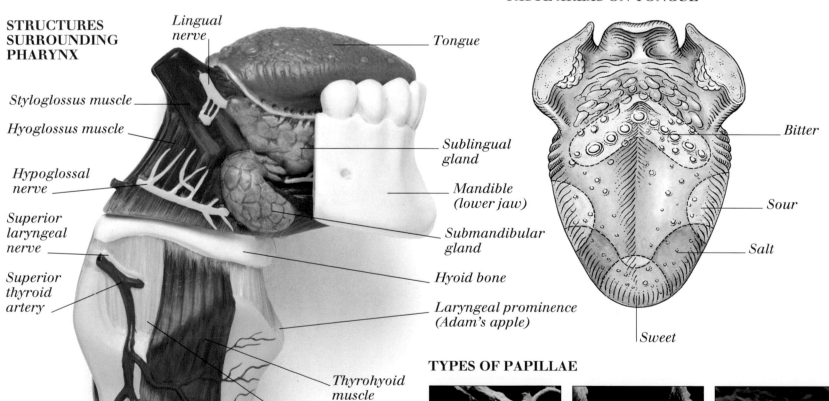

Lingual nerve
Tongue
Styloglossus muscle
Hyoglossus muscle
Sublingual gland
Hypoglossal nerve
Mandible (lower jaw)
Superior laryngeal nerve
Submandibular gland
Superior thyroid artery
Hyoid bone
Laryngeal prominence (Adam's apple)
Thyrohyoid muscle
Thyrohyoid membrane
Cricothyroid muscle
Cricothyroid ligament
Thyroid gland
Trachea

TASTE AREAS ON TONGUE

Bitter
Sour
Salt
Sweet

TYPES OF PAPILLAE

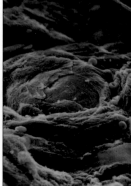

FILIFORM PAPILLAE   FUNGIFORM PAPILLAE   VALLATE PAPILLAE

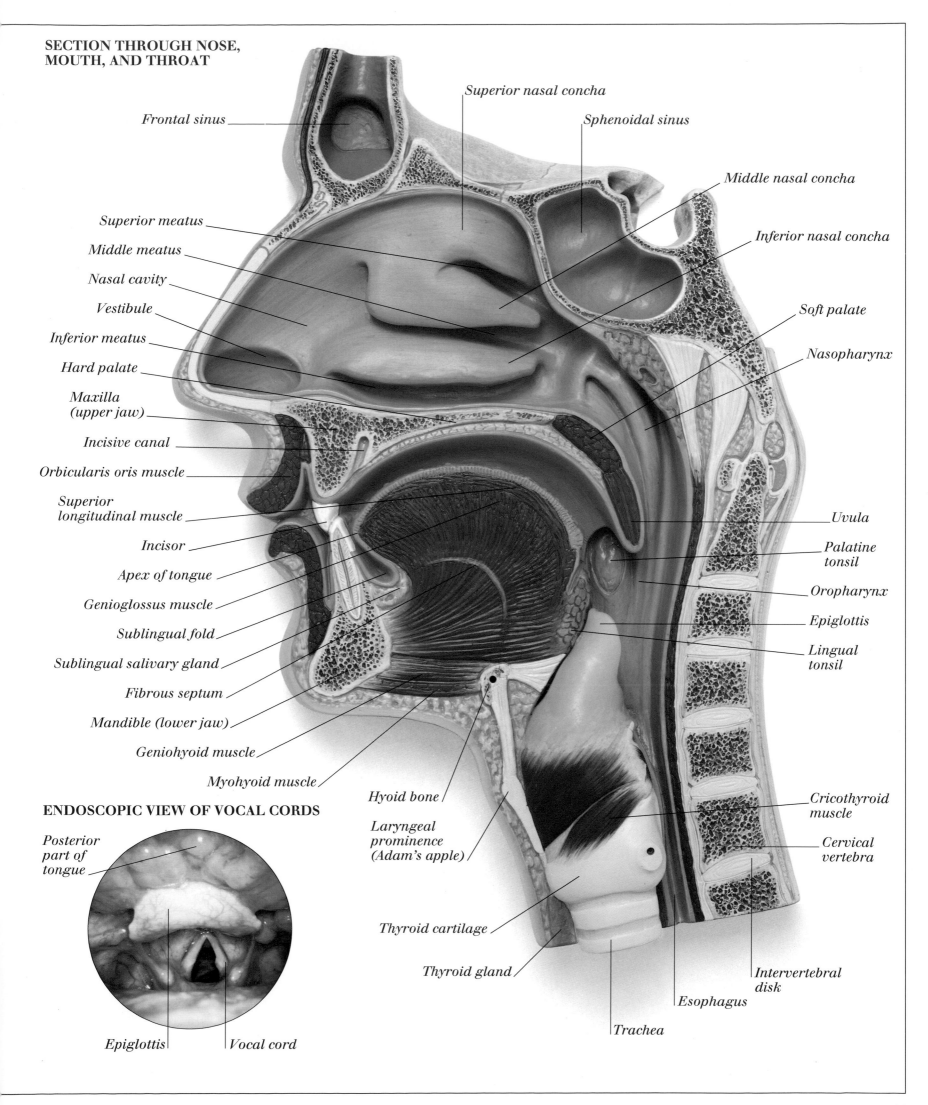

SECTION THROUGH NOSE, MOUTH, AND THROAT

Frontal sinus

Superior nasal concha

Sphenoidal sinus

Middle nasal concha

Superior meatus

Inferior nasal concha

Middle meatus

Nasal cavity

Soft palate

Vestibule

Nasopharynx

Inferior meatus

Hard palate

Maxilla (upper jaw)

Incisive canal

Orbicularis oris muscle

Uvula

Superior longitudinal muscle

Palatine tonsil

Incisor

Oropharynx

Apex of tongue

Epiglottis

Genioglossus muscle

Lingual tonsil

Sublingual fold

Sublingual salivary gland

Fibrous septum

Mandible (lower jaw)

Geniohyoid muscle

Cricothyroid muscle

Myohyoid muscle

Cervical vertebra

ENDOSCOPIC VIEW OF VOCAL CORDS

Hyoid bone

Posterior part of tongue

Laryngeal prominence (Adam's apple)

Thyroid cartilage

Intervertebral disk

Epiglottis   Vocal cord

Thyroid gland

Esophagus

Trachea

Teeth

THE 20 PRIMARY TEETH (also called deciduous or milk teeth) usually begin to erupt when a baby is about six months old. They start to be replaced by the permanent teeth when the child is about six years old. By the age of 20, most adults have a full set of 32 teeth although the third molars (commonly called wisdom teeth) may never erupt. While teeth help people to speak clearly and give shape to the face, their main function is the chewing of food. Incisors and canines shear and tear the food into pieces; premolars and molars crush and grind it further. Although tooth enamel is the hardest substance in the body, it tends to be eroded and destroyed by acid produced in the mouth during the breakdown of food.

DEVELOPMENT OF TEETH IN A FETUS

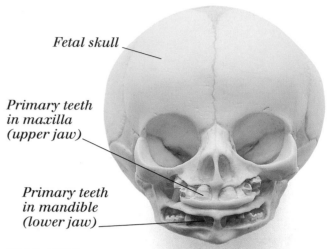

Fetal skull

Primary teeth in maxilla (upper jaw)

Primary teeth in mandible (lower jaw)

FETAL JAWS
By the sixth week of embryonic development areas of thickening occur in each jaw; these areas give rise to tooth buds. By the time the fetus is six months old, enamel has formed on the tooth buds.

DEVELOPMENT OF JAW AND TEETH

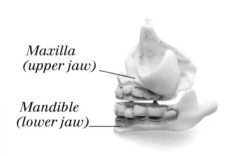

Maxilla (upper jaw)

Mandible (lower jaw)

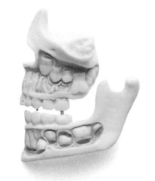

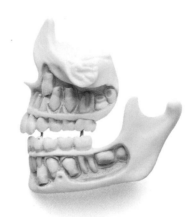

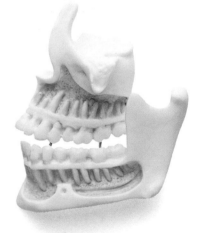

A NEWBORN BABY'S JAWS
The primary teeth can be seen developing in the jawbones; they begin to erupt around the age of six months.

A FIVE-YEAR-OLD CHILD'S TEETH
There is a full set of 20 erupted primary teeth; the permanent teeth can be seen developing in the upper and lower jaws.

A NINE-YEAR-OLD CHILD'S TEETH
Most of the teeth are primary teeth but the permanent incisors and first molars have now emerged.

AN ADULT'S TEETH
By the age of 20, the full set of 32 permanent teeth (including the wisdom teeth) should be in position.

THE PERMANENT TEETH

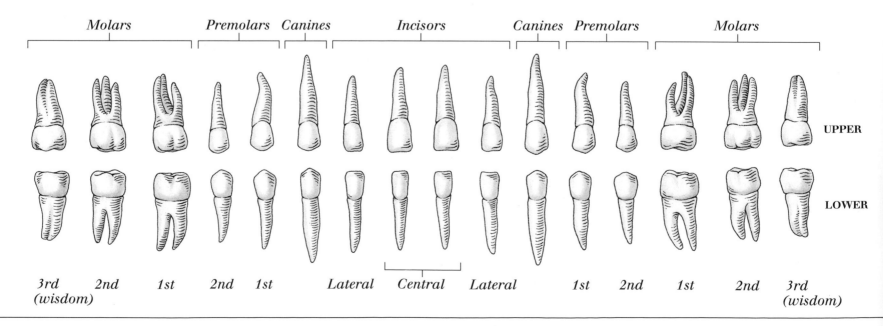

Molars   *Premolars*   *Canines*   *Incisors*   *Canines*   *Premolars*   *Molars*

UPPER

LOWER

| 3rd (wisdom) | 2nd | 1st | 2nd | 1st | Lateral | Central | Lateral | 1st | 2nd | 1st | 2nd | 3rd (wisdom) |

STRUCTURE OF A TOOTH

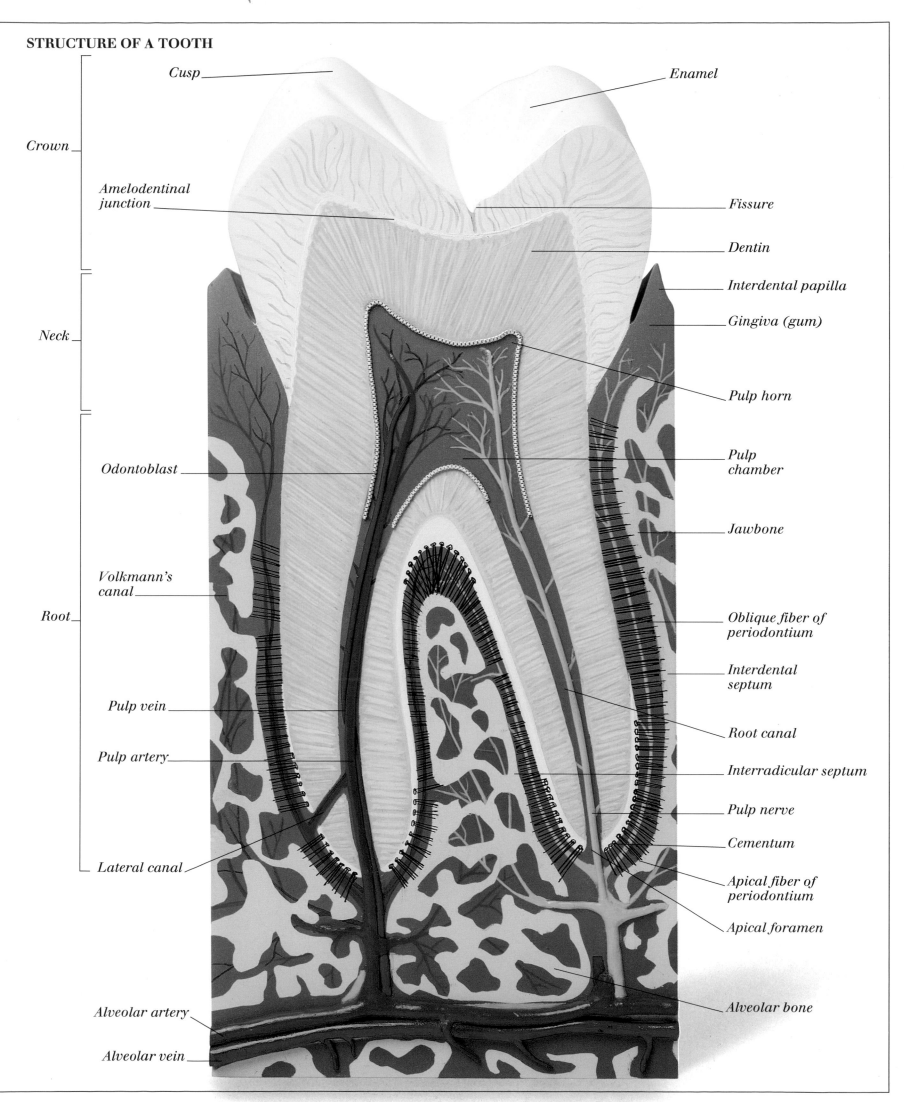

Cusp

Enamel

Crown

Amelodentinal junction

Fissure

Dentin

Neck

Interdental papilla

Gingiva (gum)

Pulp horn

Odontoblast

Pulp chamber

Jawbone

Volkmann's canal

Root

Oblique fiber of periodontium

Interdental septum

Pulp vein

Root canal

Pulp artery

Interradicular septum

Pulp nerve

Cementum

Lateral canal

Apical fiber of periodontium

Apical foramen

Alveolar bone

Alveolar artery

Alveolar vein

Digestive system 1

THE DIGESTIVE SYSTEM BREAKS DOWN FOOD into particles so tiny that blood can take nourishment to all parts of the body. The system's main part is a 30-foot (9 m) tube from mouth to rectum; muscles in this alimentary canal force food along. Chewed food first travels through the esophagus to the stomach, which churns and liquidizes food before it passes through the duodenum, jejunum, and ileum—the three parts of the long, convoluted small intestine. Here, digestive juices from the gallbladder and pancreas break down food particles; many filter out into the blood through tiny fingerlike villi that line the small intestine's inner wall. Undigested food in the colon forms feces that leave the body through the anus.

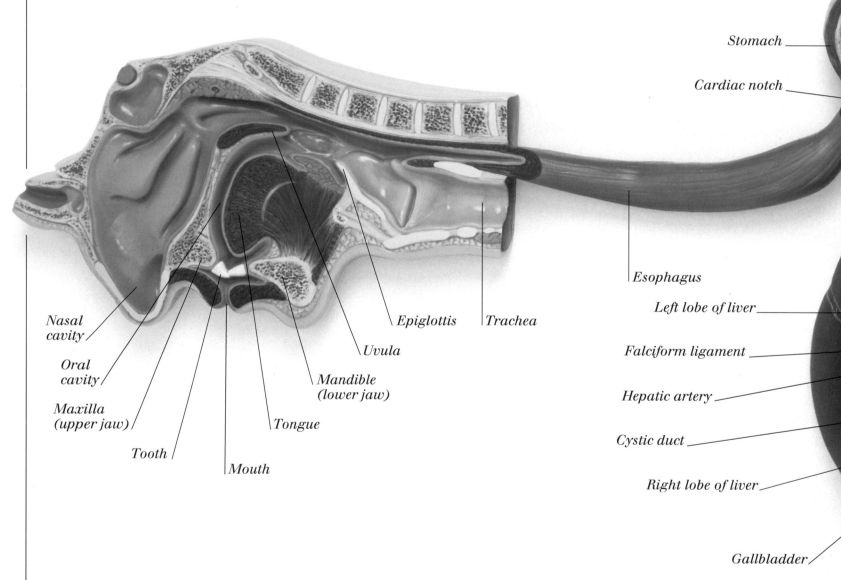

Stomach

Cardiac notch

Esophagus

Left lobe of liver

Falciform ligament

Hepatic artery

Cystic duct

Right lobe of liver

Gallbladder

Nasal cavity

Oral cavity

Maxilla (upper jaw)

Tooth

Mouth

Tongue

Mandible (lower jaw)

Uvula

Epiglottis

Trachea

ENDOSCOPIC VIEWS INSIDE ALIMENTARY CANAL

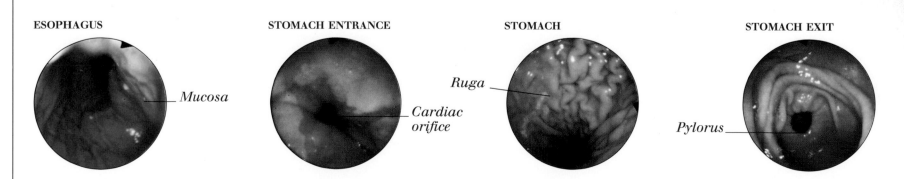

ESOPHAGUS

Mucosa

STOMACH ENTRANCE

Cardiac orifice

STOMACH

Ruga

STOMACH EXIT

Pylorus

ALIMENTARY CANAL

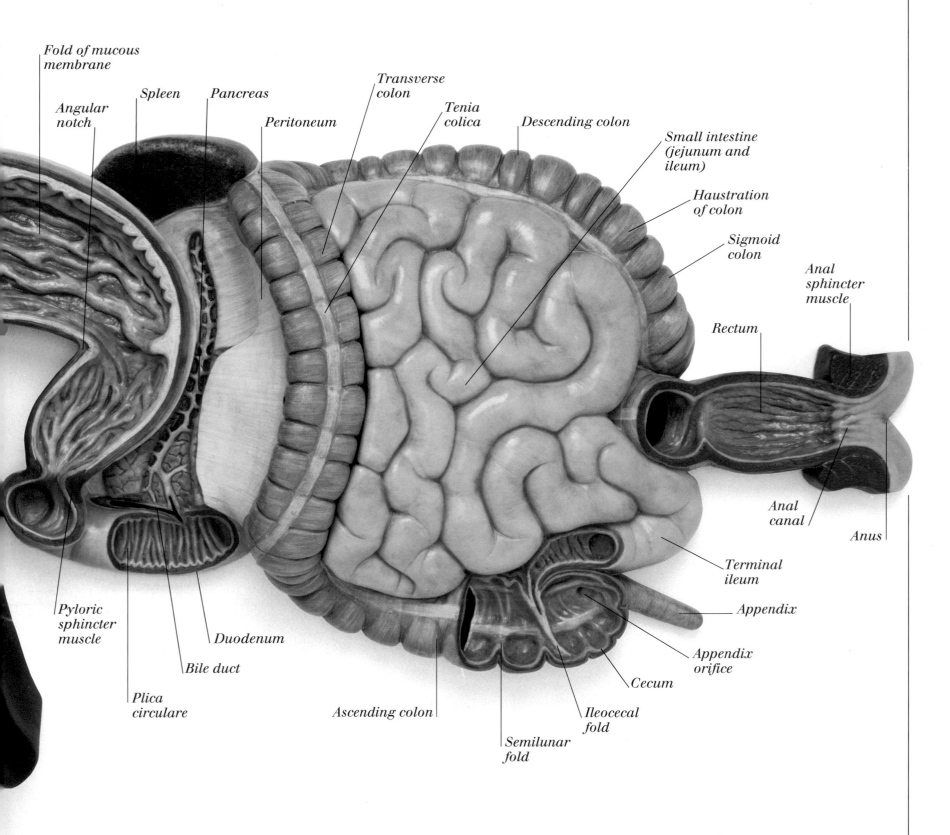

Fold of mucous membrane

Angular notch

Spleen

Pancreas

Peritoneum

Transverse colon

Tenia colica

Descending colon

Small intestine (jejunum and ileum)

Haustration of colon

Sigmoid colon

Anal sphincter muscle

Rectum

Pyloric sphincter muscle

Bile duct

Duodenum

Plica circulare

Ascending colon

Semilunar fold

Ileocecal fold

Cecum

Appendix orifice

Appendix

Terminal ileum

Anal canal

Anus

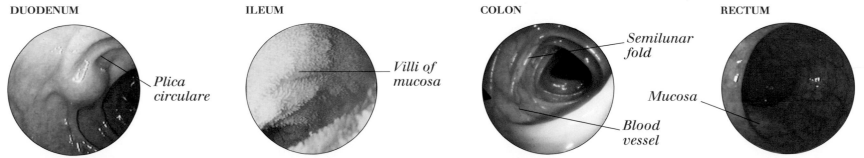

DUODENUM

Plica circulare

ILEUM

Villi of mucosa

COLON

Semilunar fold

Blood vessel

RECTUM

Mucosa

Digestive system 2

EXTERNAL ANATOMY OF STOMACH

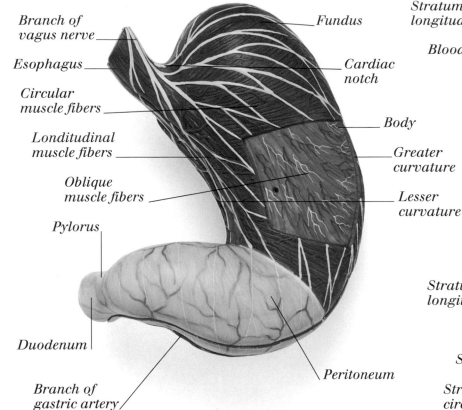

Branch of vagus nerve

Esophagus

Circular muscle fibers

Londitudinal muscle fibers

Oblique muscle fibers

Pylorus

Duodenum

Branch of gastric artery

Fundus

Cardiac notch

Body

Greater curvature

Lesser curvature

Peritoneum

STRUCTURE OF ALIMENTARY CANAL
SECTION OF ESOPHAGEAL WALL

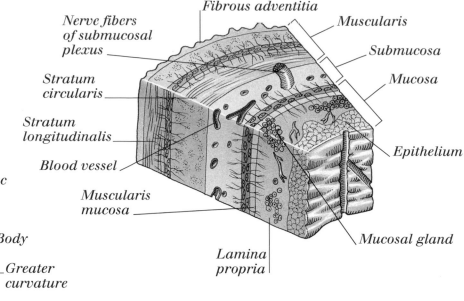

Nerve fibers of submucosal plexus

Stratum circularis

Stratum longitudinalis

Blood vessel

Muscularis mucosa

Lamina propria

Fibrous adventitia

Muscularis

Submucosa

Mucosa

Epithelium

Mucosal gland

SECTION OF STOMACH WALL

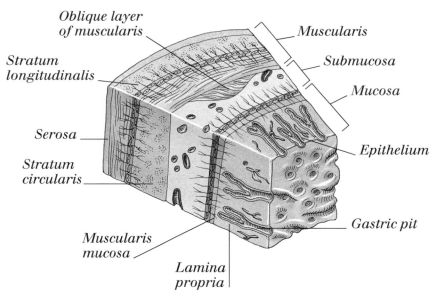

Oblique layer of muscularis

Stratum longitudinalis

Serosa

Stratum circularis

Muscularis mucosa

Lamina propria

Muscularis

Submucosa

Mucosa

Epithelium

Gastric pit

SECTION THROUGH LIVER

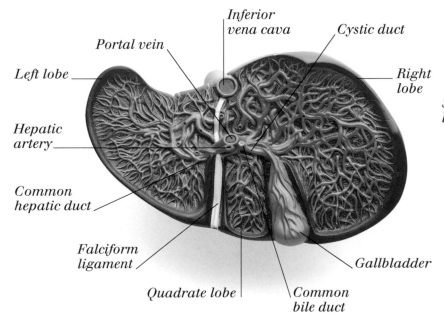

Portal vein

Left lobe

Hepatic artery

Common hepatic duct

Falciform ligament

Quadrate lobe

Inferior vena cava

Cystic duct

Right lobe

Common bile duct

Gallbladder

SECTION OF DUODENAL WALL

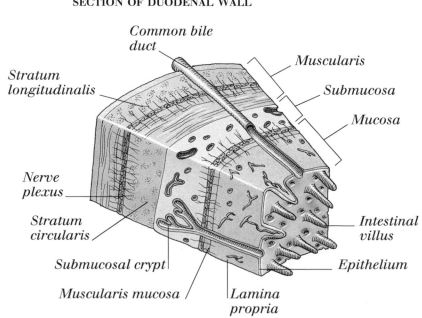

Common bile duct

Stratum longitudinalis

Nerve plexus

Stratum circularis

Submucosal crypt

Muscularis mucosa

Lamina propria

Muscularis

Submucosa

Mucosa

Intestinal villus

Epithelium

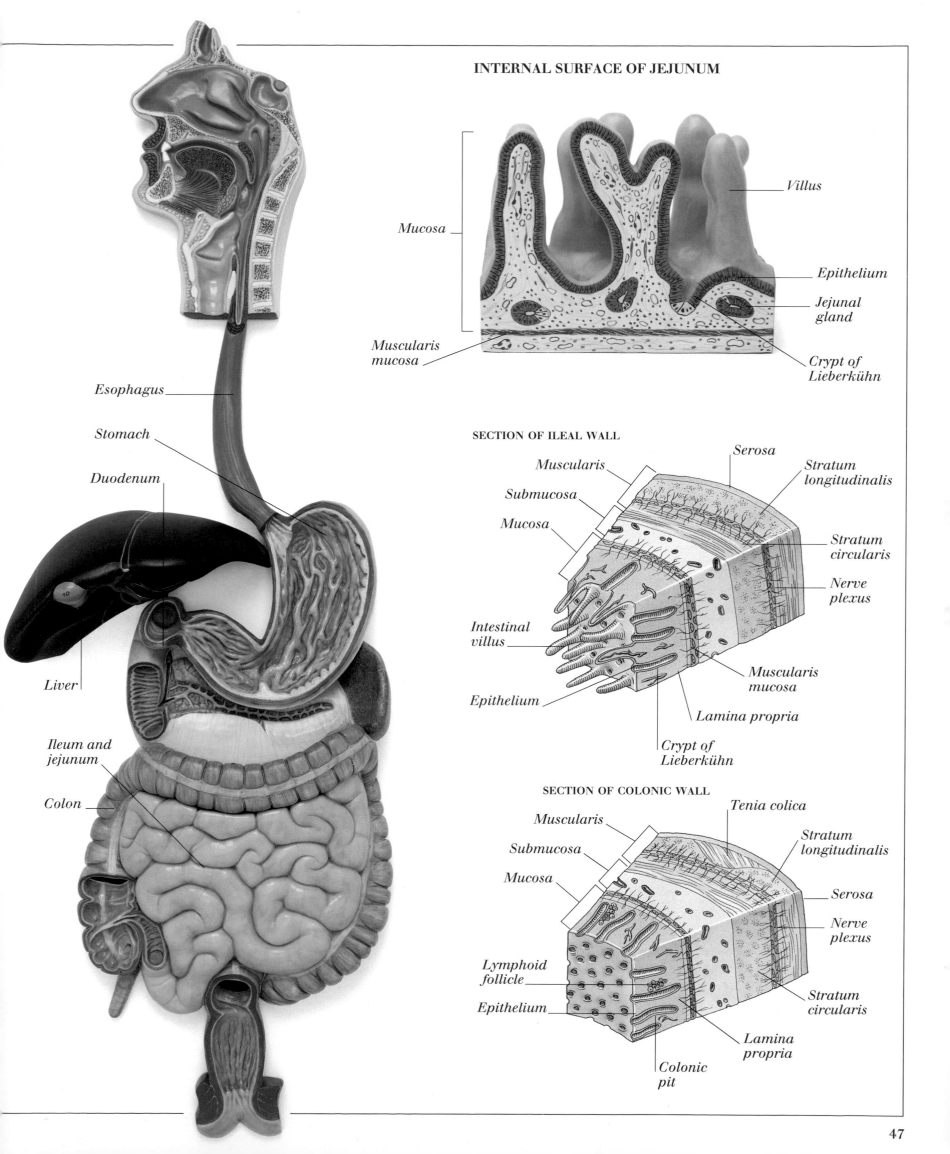

INTERNAL SURFACE OF JEJUNUM

Villus

Epithelium

Mucosa

Jejunal gland

Muscularis mucosa

Crypt of Lieberkühn

Esophagus

Stomach

Duodenum

SECTION OF ILEAL WALL

Muscularis

Serosa

Stratum longitudinalis

Submucosa

Mucosa

Stratum circularis

Nerve plexus

Liver

Intestinal villus

Muscularis mucosa

Ileum and jejunum

Epithelium

Lamina propria

Colon

Crypt of Lieberkühn

SECTION OF COLONIC WALL

Tenia colica

Muscularis

Stratum longitudinalis

Submucosa

Mucosa

Serosa

Nerve plexus

Lymphoid follicle

Stratum circularis

Epithelium

Lamina propria

Colonic pit

Heart

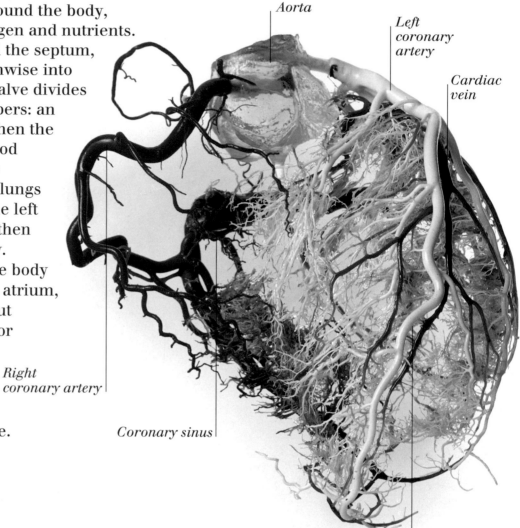

THE HEART IS A HOLLOW MUSCLE in the middle of the chest that pumps blood around the body, supplying cells with oxygen and nutrients. A muscular wall, called the septum, divides the heart lengthwise into left and right sides. A valve divides each side into two chambers: an upper atrium and a lower ventricle. When the heart muscle contracts, it squeezes blood through the atria and then through the ventricles. Oxygenated blood from the lungs flows from the pulmonary veins into the left atrium, through the left ventricle, and then out via the aorta to all parts of the body. Deoxygenated blood returning from the body flows from the vena cava into the right atrium, through the right ventricle, and then out via the pulmonary artery to the lungs for reoxygenation. At rest the heart beats between 60 and 80 times a minute; during exercise or at times of stress or excitement the rate may increase to 200 beats a minute.

ARTERIES AND VEINS SURROUNDING HEART

Aorta

Left coronary artery

Cardiac vein

Right coronary artery

Coronary sinus

Main branch of left coronary artery

SECTION THROUGH HEART WALL

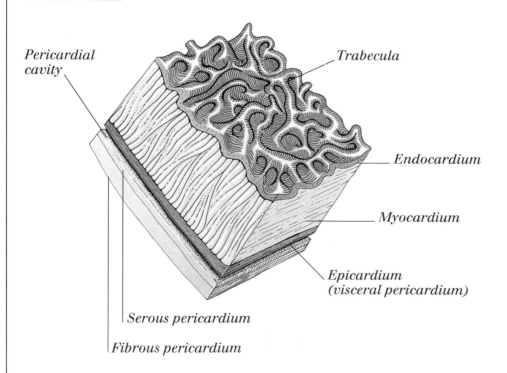

Pericardial cavity

Trabecula

Endocardium

Myocardium

Epicardium (visceral pericardium)

Serous pericardium

Fibrous pericardium

HEARTBEAT SEQUENCE

ATRIAL DIASTOLE

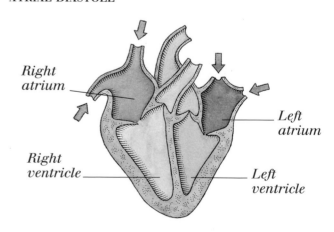

Right atrium

Left atrium

Right ventricle

Left ventricle

Deoxygenated blood enters the right atrium while the left atrium receives oxygenated blood.

STRUCTURE OF HEART

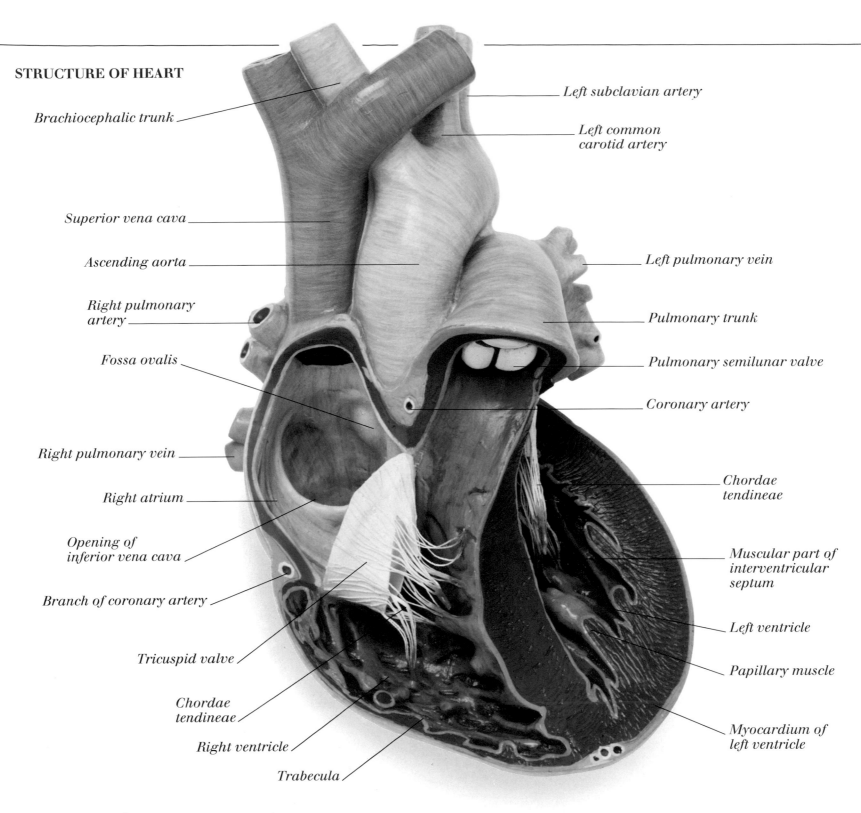

Brachiocephalic trunk

Left subclavian artery

Left common carotid artery

Superior vena cava

Ascending aorta

Right pulmonary artery

Fossa ovalis

Right pulmonary vein

Right atrium

Opening of inferior vena cava

Branch of coronary artery

Tricuspid valve

Chordae tendineae

Right ventricle

Trabecula

Left pulmonary vein

Pulmonary trunk

Pulmonary semilunar valve

Coronary artery

Chordae tendineae

Muscular part of interventricular septum

Left ventricle

Papillary muscle

Myocardium of left ventricle

ATRIAL SYSTOLE (VENTRICULAR DIASTOLE)

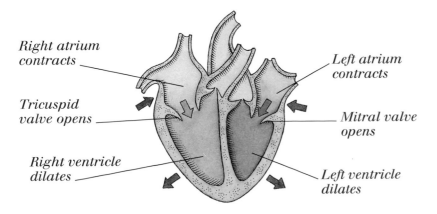

Right atrium contracts

Tricuspid valve opens

Right ventricle dilates

Left atrium contracts

Mitral valve opens

Left ventricle dilates

Left and right atria contract, forcing blood into the relaxed ventricles.

VENTRICULAR SYSTOLE

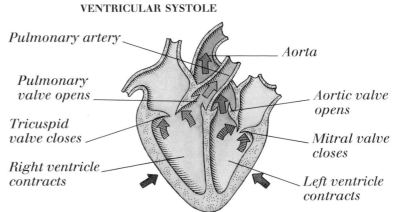

Pulmonary artery

Pulmonary valve opens

Tricuspid valve closes

Right ventricle contracts

Aorta

Aortic valve opens

Mitral valve closes

Left ventricle contracts

Ventricles contract and force blood to the lungs for oxygenation and via the aorta to the rest of the body.

Circulatory system

THE CIRCULATORY SYSTEM consists of the heart and blood vessels, which together maintain a continuous flow of blood around the body. The heart pumps oxygen-rich blood from the lungs to all parts of the body through a network of tubes called arteries, and smaller branches called arterioles. Blood returns to the heart via small vessels called venules, which lead in turn into larger tubes called veins. Arterioles and venules are linked by a network of tiny vessels called capillaries, where the exchange of oxygen and carbon dioxide between blood and body cells takes place. Blood has four main components: red blood cells, white blood cells, platelets, and liquid plasma.

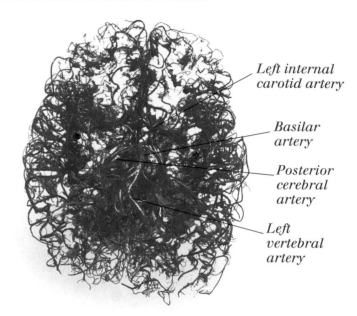

ARTERIAL SYSTEM OF BRAIN

Left internal carotid artery

Basilar artery

Posterior cerebral artery

Left vertebral artery

CIRCULATORY SYSTEM OF LIVER

Inferior vena cava

Portal vein

Common bile duct

Hepatic artery

Gallbladder

CIRCULATORY SYSTEM OF HEART AND LUNGS

Superior vena cava

Aorta

Right ventricle

Left ventricle

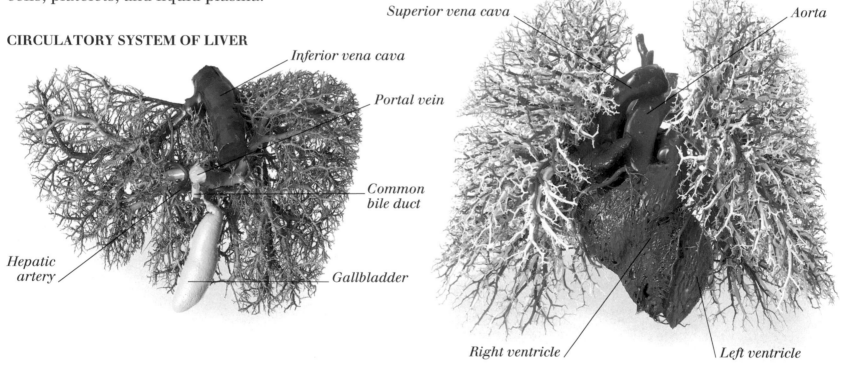

SECTION OF MAIN ARTERY

Tunica media

Collagen and elastic fibers

External elastic lamina

Tunica adventitia

Internal elastic lamina

Tunica intima

Endothelium

Arteriole

SECTION OF MAIN VEIN

Tunica media

Collagen and elastic fibers

External elastic lamina

Tunica adventitia

Valve cusp

Internal elastic lamina

Tunica intima

Endothelium

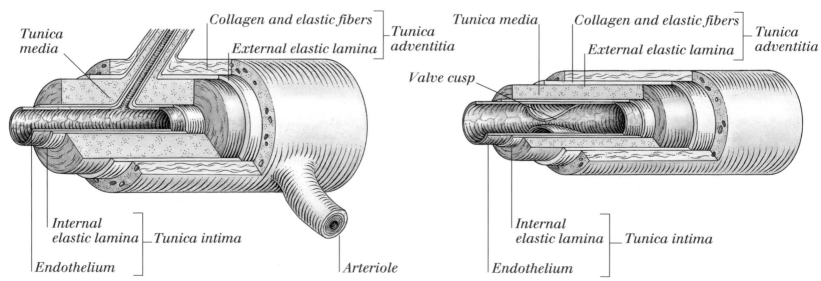

PRINCIPAL ARTERIES AND VEINS OF CIRCULATORY SYSTEM

Common carotid artery

Subclavian artery

Arch of aorta

Axillary artery

Pulmonary artery

Coronary artery

Brachial artery

Gastric artery

Hepatic artery

Splenic artery

Superior mesenteric artery

Radial artery

Ulnar artery

Palmar arch

Digital artery

Common iliac artery

External iliac artery

Internal iliac artery

Femoral artery

Popliteal artery

Peroneal artery

Anterior tibial artery

Posterior tibial artery

Lateral plantar artery

Dorsal metatarsal artery

Internal jugular vein

Brachiocephalic vein

Subclavian vein

Axillary vein

Cephalic vein

Superior vena cava

Pulmonary vein

Basilic vein

Hepatic portal vein

Median cubital vein

Inferior vena cava

Anterior median vein

Gastroepiploic vein

Palmar vein

Digital vein

Inferior mesenteric vein

Superior mesenteric vein

Common iliac vein

External iliac vein

Internal iliac vein

Femoral vein

Great saphenous vein

Short saphenous vein

Dorsal venous arch

Digital vein

TYPES OF BLOOD CELLS

RED BLOOD CELLS
These cells are biconcave in shape to maximize their oxygen-carrying capacity.

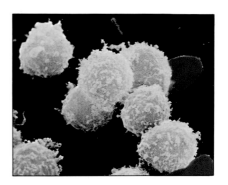

WHITE BLOOD CELLS
Lymphocytes are the smallest white blood cells; they form antibodies against disease.

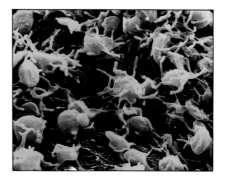

PLATELETS
Tiny cells that are activated whenever blood clotting or repair to vessels is necessary.

BLOOD CLOTTING

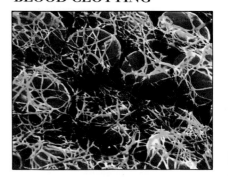

Filaments of fibrin enmesh red blood cells as part of the process of blood clotting.

51

Respiratory system

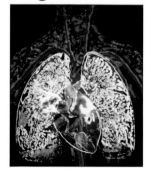

THE RESPIRATORY SYSTEM supplies the oxygen needed by body cells and carries off their carbon dioxide waste. Inhaled air passes via the trachea (windpipe) through two narrower tubes, the bronchi, to the lungs. Each lung comprises many fine, branching tubes called bronchioles that end in tiny clustered chambers called alveoli. Gases cross the thin alveolar walls to and from a network of tiny blood vessels. Intercostal (rib) muscles and the muscular diaphragm below the lungs operate the lungs like bellows, drawing air in and forcing it out at regular intervals.

BRONCHIOLE AND ALVEOLI

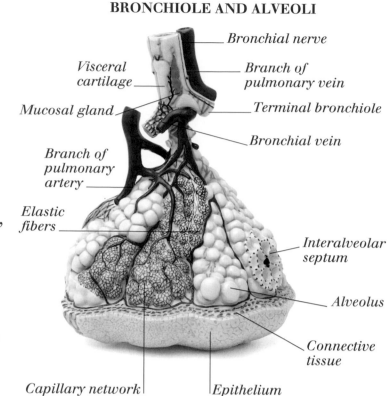

Bronchial nerve

Visceral cartilage

Branch of pulmonary vein

Mucosal gland

Terminal bronchiole

Branch of pulmonary artery

Bronchial vein

Elastic fibers

Interalveolar septum

Alveolus

Connective tissue

Capillary network

Epithelium

SEGMENTS OF BRONCHIAL TREE

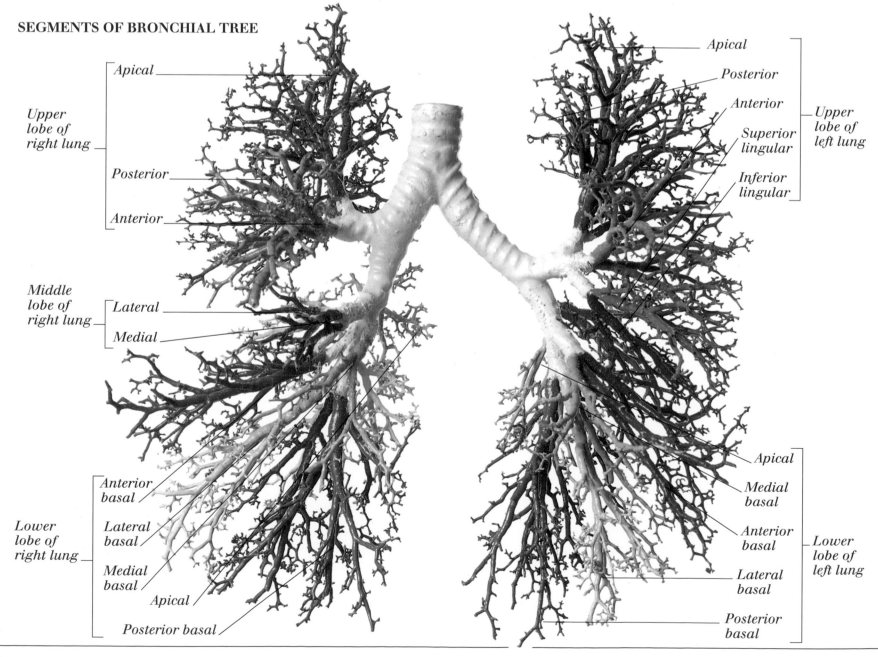

Apical

Posterior

Anterior

Superior lingular

Inferior lingular

Upper lobe of left lung

Upper lobe of right lung

Apical

Posterior

Anterior

Middle lobe of right lung

Lateral

Medial

Apical

Medial basal

Anterior basal

Lateral basal

Lower lobe of left lung

Anterior basal

Lateral basal

Medial basal

Apical

Lower lobe of right lung

Posterior basal

Posterior basal

STRUCTURES OF THORACIC CAVITY

Epiglottis

Hyoid bone

Thyroid cartilage

Thyroid gland

Cricoid cartilage

Apex of lung

Trachea

Superior vena cava

Aorta

Upper lobe of right lung

Upper lobe of left lung

Horizontal fissure

Pulmonary trunk

Oblique fissure

Left pulmonary artery

Heart

Lower lobe of left lung

Secondary bronchus

Tertiary bronchus

Muscular wall of diaphragm

Lower lobe of right lung

Middle lobe of right lung

Right crus of diaphragm

Abdominal aorta

Left crus of diaphragm

Esophagus

GASEOUS EXCHANGE IN ALVEOLUS

Oxygen diffuses into blood

Oxygenated blood

Alveolus

Deoxygenated blood rich in carbon dioxide

Carbon dioxide diffuses from blood into alveolus

MECHANISM OF RESPIRATION

INSPIRATION

Lung expands

Air drawn into lungs

Diaphragm contracts and flattens

Intercostal muscles contract

EXPIRATION

Lung contracts

Air forced out of lungs

Diaphragm relaxes and moves up

Intercostal muscles relax

Urinary system

THE URINARY SYSTEM FILTERS WASTE PRODUCTS from the blood and removes them from the body via a system of tubes. Blood is filtered in the two kidneys, which are fist-sized, bean-shaped organs. The renal arteries carry blood to the kidneys; the renal veins remove blood after filtering. Each kidney contains about one million tiny units called nephrons. Each nephron is made up of a tubule and a filtering unit called a glomerulus, which consists of a collection of tiny blood vessels surrounded by the hollow Bowman's capsule. The filtering process produces a watery fluid that leaves the kidney as urine. The urine is carried via two tubes called ureters to the bladder, where it is stored until its release from the body through another tube called the urethra.

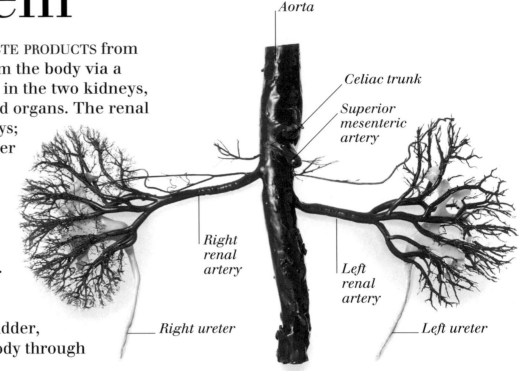

ARTERIAL SYSTEM OF KIDNEYS

Aorta

Celiac trunk

Superior mesenteric artery

Right renal artery

Left renal artery

Right ureter

Left ureter

SECTION THROUGH LEFT KIDNEY

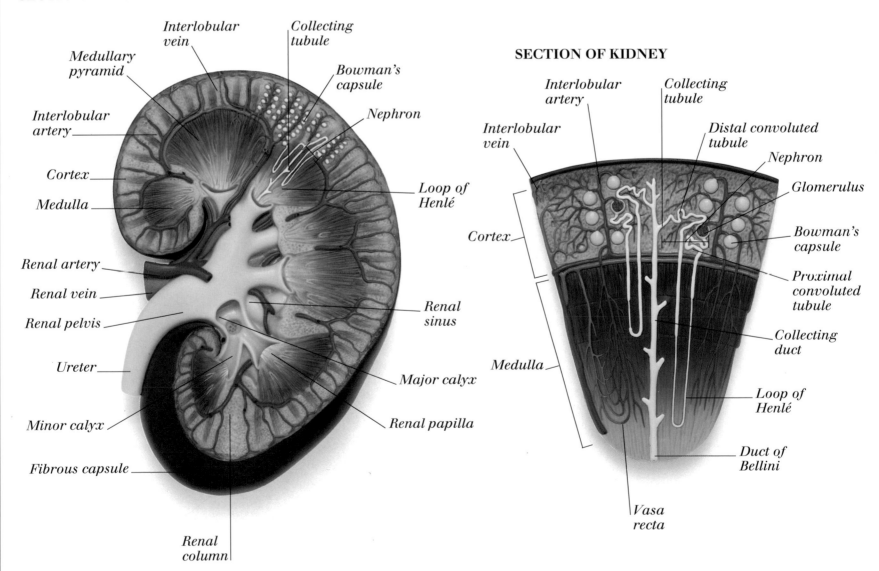

Interlobular vein

Collecting tubule

Medullary pyramid

Bowman's capsule

Interlobular artery

Nephron

Cortex

Medulla

Loop of Henlé

Renal artery

Renal vein

Renal pelvis

Renal sinus

Ureter

Major calyx

Minor calyx

Renal papilla

Fibrous capsule

Renal column

SECTION OF KIDNEY

Interlobular artery

Collecting tubule

Interlobular vein

Distal convoluted tubule

Nephron

Glomerulus

Cortex

Bowman's capsule

Proximal convoluted tubule

Collecting duct

Medulla

Loop of Henlé

Duct of Bellini

Vasa recta

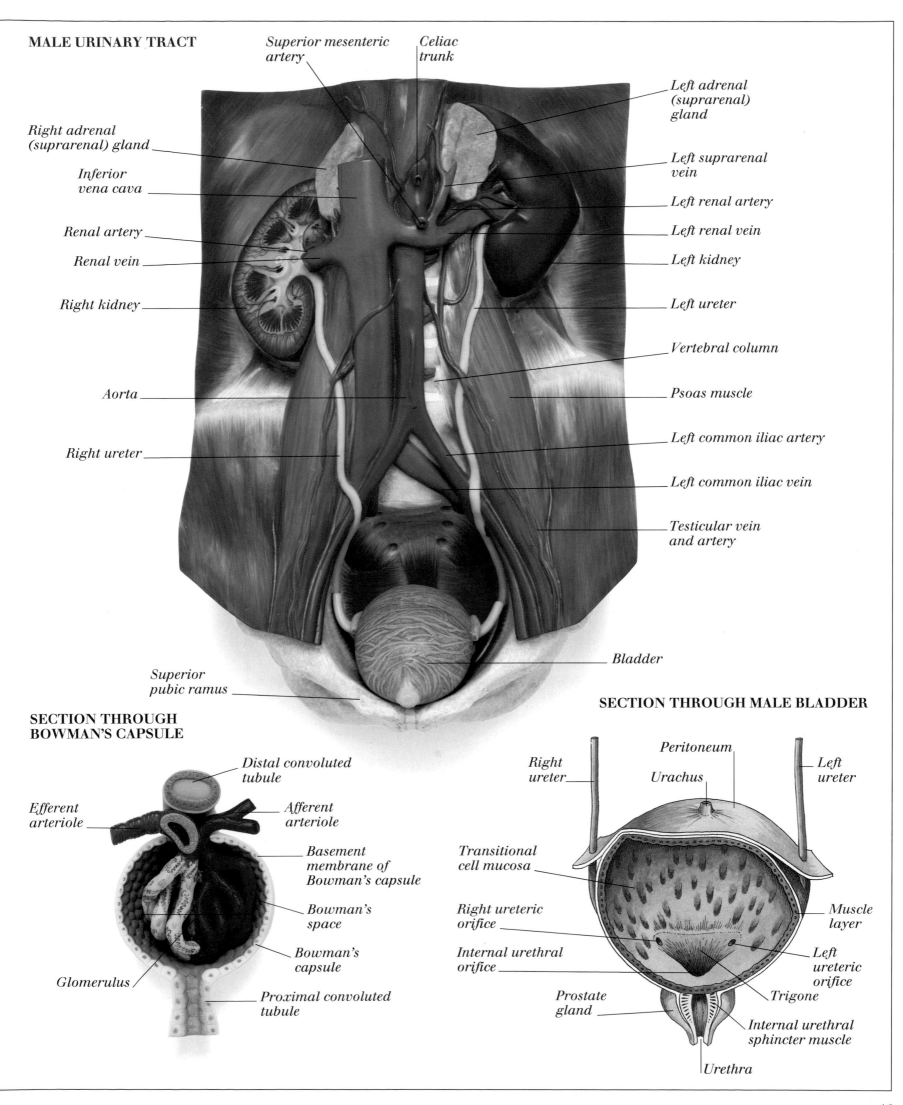

MALE URINARY TRACT

Superior mesenteric artery

Celiac trunk

Left adrenal (suprarenal) gland

Right adrenal (suprarenal) gland

Inferior vena cava

Left suprarenal vein

Left renal artery

Renal artery

Left renal vein

Renal vein

Left kidney

Right kidney

Left ureter

Vertebral column

Aorta

Psoas muscle

Left common iliac artery

Right ureter

Left common iliac vein

Testicular vein and artery

Bladder

Superior pubic ramus

SECTION THROUGH MALE BLADDER

SECTION THROUGH BOWMAN'S CAPSULE

Distal convoluted tubule

Efferent arteriole

Afferent arteriole

Basement membrane of Bowman's capsule

Bowman's space

Bowman's capsule

Glomerulus

Proximal convoluted tubule

Right ureter

Peritoneum

Urachus

Left ureter

Transitional cell mucosa

Right ureteric orifice

Muscle layer

Internal urethral orifice

Left ureteric orifice

Prostate gland

Trigone

Internal urethral sphincter muscle

Urethra

Reproductive system

SEX ORGANS LOCATED IN THE PELVIS create new human lives. Each month a ripe egg is released from one of the female's ovaries into a fallopian tube leading to the uterus (womb), a muscular pear-sized organ. A male produces minute tadpole-like sperm in two oval glands called testes. When the male is ready to release sperm into the female's vagina, many millions pass into his urethra and leave his body through the fleshy penis. The sperm travel up through the vagina into the uterus and one sperm may enter and fertilize an egg. The fertilized egg becomes embedded in the uterus wall and starts to grow into a new human being.

SECTION THROUGH OVARY

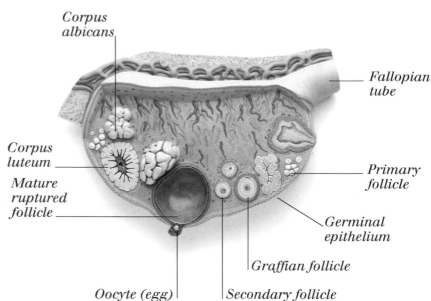

Corpus albicans

Fallopian tube

Corpus luteum

Mature ruptured follicle

Primary follicle

Germinal epithelium

Graffian follicle

Secondary follicle

Oocyte (egg)

SECTION THROUGH FEMALE PELVIC REGION

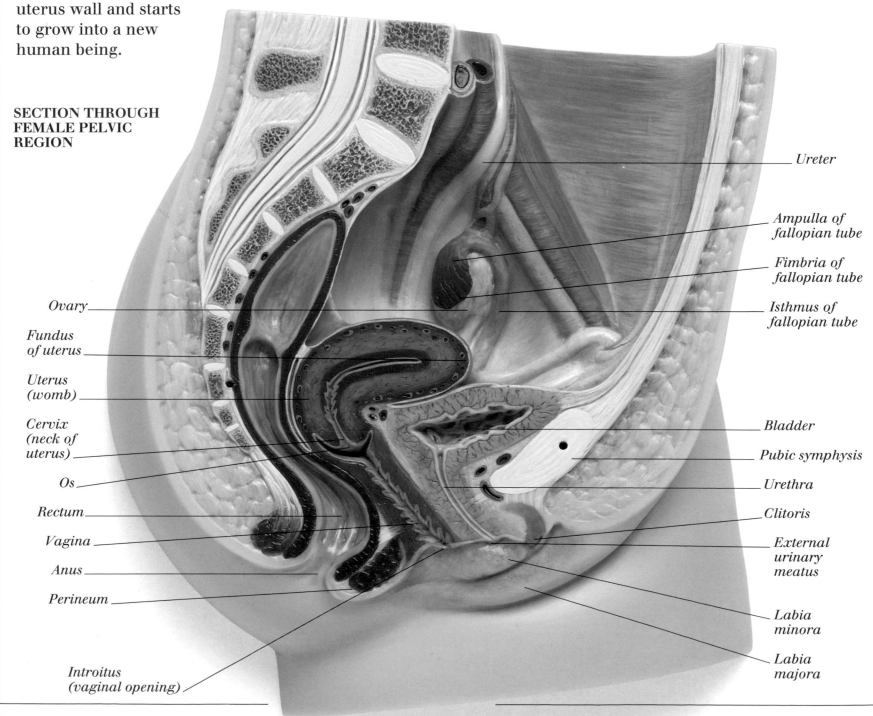

Ureter

Ampulla of fallopian tube

Fimbria of fallopian tube

Isthmus of fallopian tube

Ovary

Fundus of uterus

Uterus (womb)

Cervix (neck of uterus)

Os

Rectum

Vagina

Anus

Perineum

Introitus (vaginal opening)

Bladder

Pubic symphysis

Urethra

Clitoris

External urinary meatus

Labia minora

Labia majora

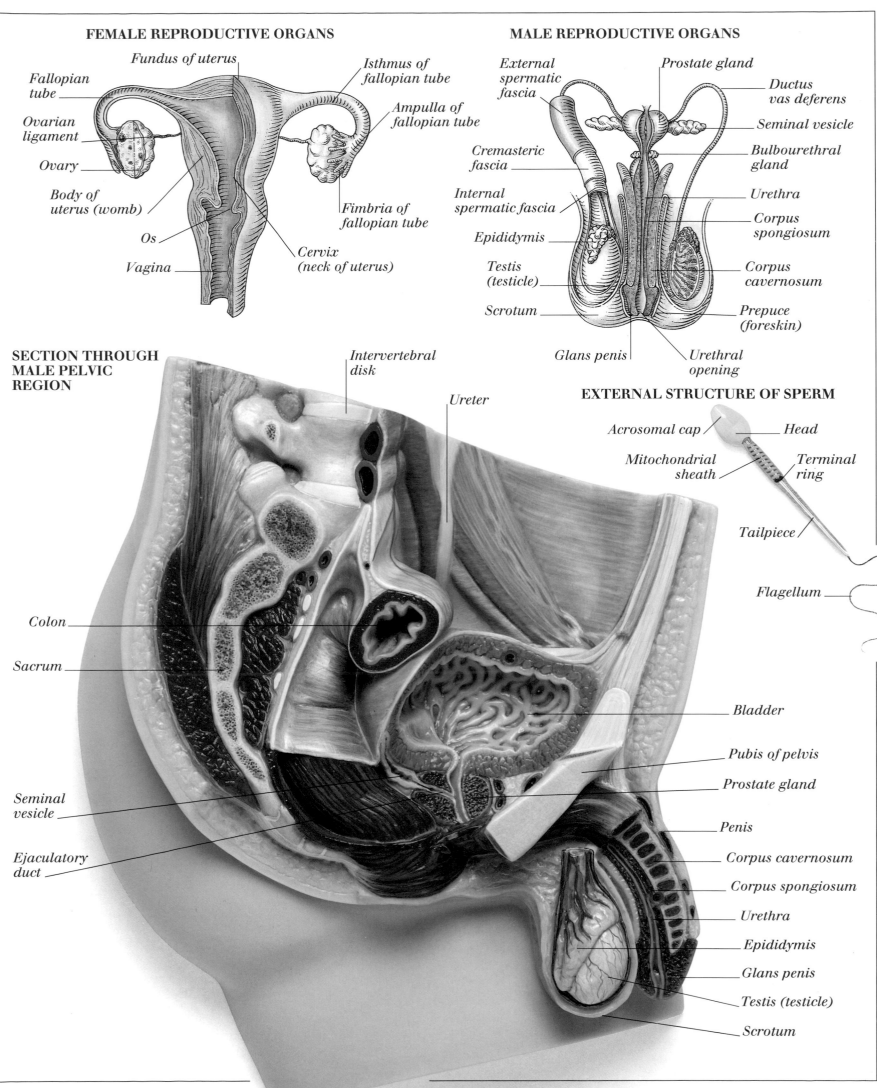

FEMALE REPRODUCTIVE ORGANS

Fallopian tube
Fundus of uterus
Isthmus of fallopian tube
Ovarian ligament
Ampulla of fallopian tube
Ovary
Body of uterus (womb)
Fimbria of fallopian tube
Os
Cervix (neck of uterus)
Vagina

MALE REPRODUCTIVE ORGANS

External spermatic fascia
Prostate gland
Ductus vas deferens
Cremasteric fascia
Seminal vesicle
Bulbourethral gland
Internal spermatic fascia
Urethra
Epididymis
Corpus spongiosum
Testis (testicle)
Corpus cavernosum
Scrotum
Prepuce (foreskin)
Glans penis
Urethral opening

SECTION THROUGH MALE PELVIC REGION

Intervertebral disk
Ureter

Colon
Sacrum
Seminal vesicle
Ejaculatory duct

EXTERNAL STRUCTURE OF SPERM

Acrosomal cap
Head
Mitochondrial sheath
Terminal ring
Tailpiece
Flagellum

Bladder
Pubis of pelvis
Prostate gland
Penis
Corpus cavernosum
Corpus spongiosum
Urethra
Epididymis
Glans penis
Testis (testicle)
Scrotum

Development of a baby

A FERTILIZED EGG IS NOURISHED AND PROTECTED as it
develops into an embryo and then a fetus during the 40
weeks of pregnancy. The placenta, a mass of blood vessels
implanted in the uterus lining, delivers nourishment and
oxygen, and removes waste through the umbilical cord.
Meanwhile, the fetus lies snugly in its amniotic sac, a bag of
fluid that protects it against any sudden jolts. In the last
weeks of the pregnancy, the rapidly growing fetus turns
head down: a baby ready to be born.

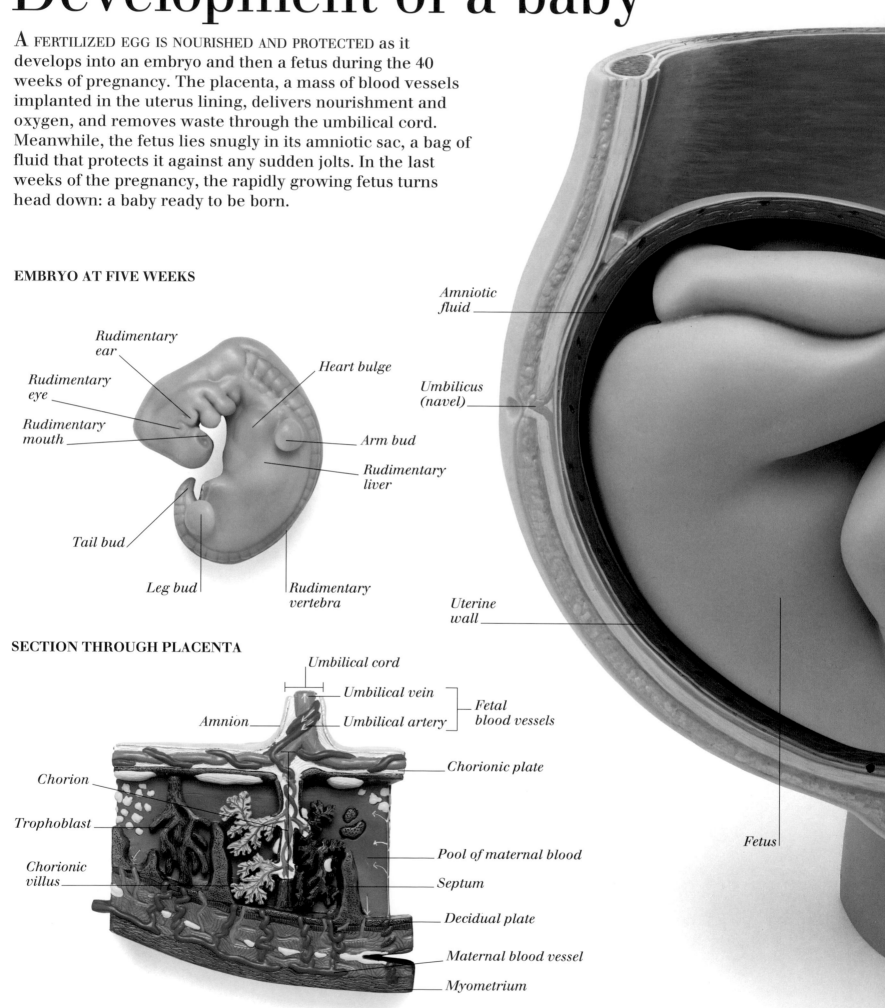

EMBRYO AT FIVE WEEKS

Rudimentary
ear

Rudimentary
eye

Rudimentary
mouth

Heart bulge

Arm bud

Rudimentary
liver

Tail bud

Leg bud

Rudimentary
vertebra

Amniotic
fluid

Umbilicus
(navel)

Uterine
wall

Fetus

SECTION THROUGH PLACENTA

Umbilical cord

Umbilical vein

Umbilical artery

Fetal
blood vessels

Amnion

Chorion

Trophoblast

Chorionic
villus

Chorionic plate

Pool of maternal blood

Septum

Decidual plate

Maternal blood vessel

Myometrium

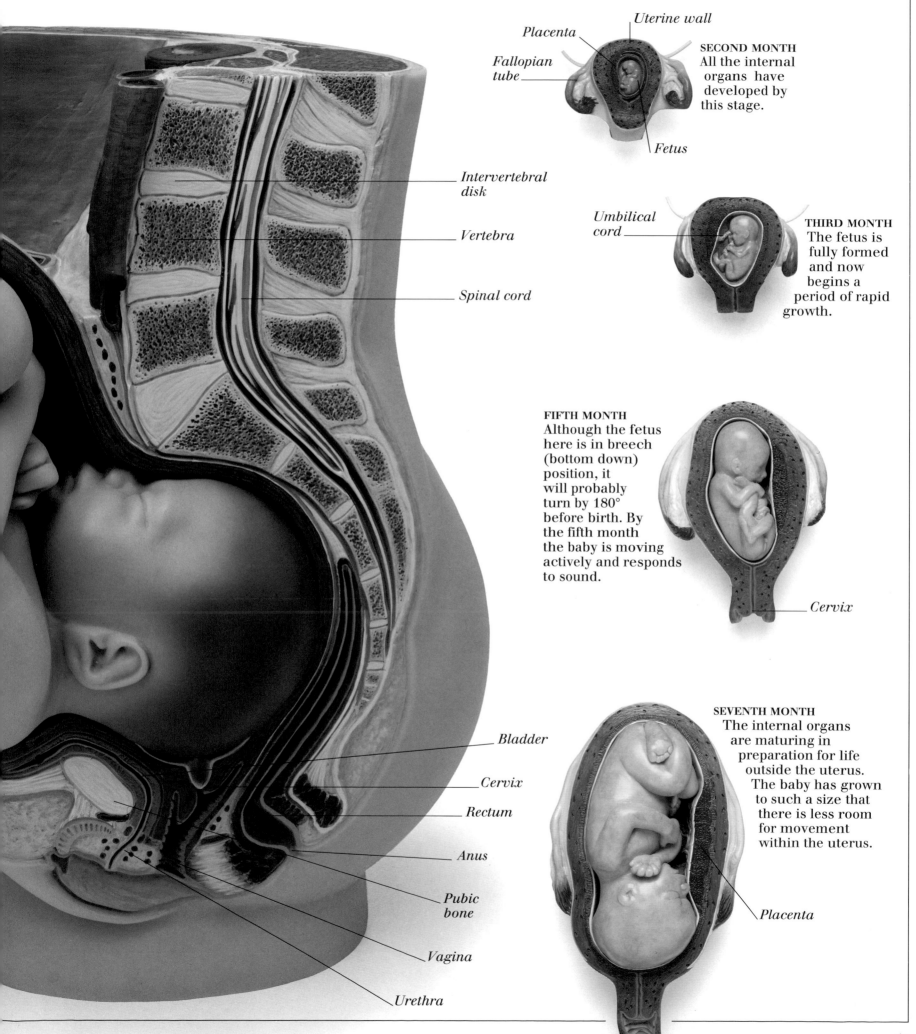

SECTION THROUGH PELVIS IN NINTH MONTH OF PREGNANCY

THE DEVELOPING FETUS

Placenta

Uterine wall

Fallopian tube

SECOND MONTH All the internal organs have developed by this stage.

Fetus

Intervertebral disk

Vertebra

Spinal cord

Umbilical cord

THIRD MONTH The fetus is fully formed and now begins a period of rapid growth.

FIFTH MONTH Although the fetus here is in breech (bottom down) position, it will probably turn by 180° before birth. By the fifth month the baby is moving actively and responds to sound.

Cervix

Bladder

Cervix

Rectum

Anus

SEVENTH MONTH The internal organs are maturing in preparation for life outside the uterus. The baby has grown to such a size that there is less room for movement within the uterus.

Pubic bone

Vagina

Placenta

Urethra

Index

Acknowledgments

Dorling Kindersley would like to thank :
Derek Edwards and Dr Martin Collins, British School
of Osteopathy for skeletal material and advice;
Dr M.C.E. Hutchinson, Department of Anatomy,
United Medical and Dental Schools of Guy's and
St Thomas' Hospitals for resin casts, additional
skeletal material, and advice; models Barry O'Rorke
(Bodyline Agency) and Pauline Swaine (MOT Model
Agency).

Additional editorial assistance:
Susan Bosanko, Candace Burch, Deirdre Clark, Paul
Docherty, Edwina Johnson, David Lambert, Gail
Lawther, Dr Robert Youngson

Additional models
Bodyline, Donkin Models, Gordon Models, Morrison
Frederick

Additional photography:
Dave Rudkin

Illustrators:
Simone End, Roy Flooks, David Gardner, Mick
Gillah, Dave Hopkins, Linden Artists, John Woodcock

Index:
Dr Robert Youngson

Picture credits:
a=above, b=below, c=center, J=jacket, l=left,
m=middle, r=right, t=top
Biophoto Associates: pages 13ca, cra, 24cbc, cbm,
26tr
KeyMed Ltd: 44bl, 45bl, bcl
Dr D.N. Landon (Institute of Neurology): 24bl, br
Life Science Images (Ron Boardman): 40bl, br
National Medical Slide Bank: 13cr

Science Photo Library: 10brc, 32; /Michael Abbey:
21t; /Agfa: Jct, 16tl; /Biophoto Associates: 13crb; /Dr
Jeremy Burgess: 31bcl; /CNRI:10tl, cl, c, cr, bl, clb,
crb, blc, br, 13cb, 31bcr, 34tl, 45bcr, 51tr, cra, 54tl; /
Dr Brian Eyden: 24cbr; /Professor C. Ferlaud: 41clb; /
Simon Fraser; 10 bcl; /Eric Grave: 13br; /Jan Hinsch:
21tc; /Manfred Kage: 13c, 31br, 33b; /Astrid and
Hans-Freider Michler: 13tr; /NIBSC: 51br; /Omikron:
40bc; /David Scharf: 31bl; /Dr Klaus Schiller: 44bcl,
bcr, br; /Secchi-Lecaque/Roussel-UCLAF/CNRI: 13tc,
51crb;/Stammers/Thompson: 26tl; /Sheila Terry: 30tl
Dr Christopher B. Williams (St Mark's Hospital): 45br
Dr Robert Youngson: 37cr
Zefa: 13bc; /H. Sochurek: Jcb, 6tl, 10cb, bcr, 48tl, 52tl

Picture research:
Sandra Schneider